The Institute of Biology's
Studies in Biology no 58

Ecology of Plants
in the Tropics

Daniel H. Janzen

Department of Ecology and Evolutionary Biology
University of Michigan

Edward Arnold

First published 1975
by Edward Arnold (Publishers) Ltd.,
25 Hill Street, London W1X 8LL

Boards edition ISBN 0 7131 2481 4
Paper edition ISBN 0 7131 2482 2

Printed in Great Britain by
Butler & Tanner Ltd, Frome and London

General Preface to the Series

It is no longer possible for one textbook to cover the whole field of Biology and to remain sufficiently up-to-date. At the same time teachers and students at school, college or university need to keep abreast of recent trends and know where significant developments are taking place.

To meet the need for this progressive approach the Institute of Biology has for some years sponsored this series of booklets dealing with subjects specially selected by a panel of editors. The enthusiastic acceptance of the series by teachers and students at school, college and university shows the usefulness of the books in providing a clear and up-to-date coverage of topics, particularly in areas of research and changing views.

Among the features of the series are the attention given to methods, the inclusion of a selected list of books for reading and, wherever possible, suggestions for practical work.

Readers' comments will be welcomed by the authors or the Education Officer of the Institute.

1975

The Institute of Biology,
41 Queen's Gate,
London, SW7 5IIU

ACKNOWLEDGEMENTS

This book owes much of its conceptual development to discussions with students and faculty of courses taught by the Organization for Tropical Studies between 1965 and 1973. Financial support was provided by National Science Foundation Grant GB-35032X. Invaluable logistic support was provided by C. M. Pond, D. A. Pond and M. H. Pond, and by the Hope Department of Entomology and the Department of Zoology, Oxford. C. M. Pond added invaluable editorial comments.

Introduction

It is my opinion that the study of plant biology in general, and the biology of tropical plants in particular, has suffered greatly from over emphasis on descriptive morphology, phytosociology, and systematics. Here, I attempt to present an inquiry with an ecological and evolutionary bias. We understand almost nothing of the adaptive significance of the behaviour and morphology of most tropical plants, and the ecological why of the physiology of wild tropical plants is equally unclear. There is a whole new world awaiting the person who determines what individual plants actually do and what intra-population variation there is in these characteristics. Such a study must, however, take great care to distinguish between the environmental cues used by a plant and the selective pressures that led to a plant phenotype that would respond to those cues. The more tropical the habitat, the more relevant this warning.

This book deals almost entirely with angiosperms. This is partly due to my own field experience with these plants, and partly due to the conspicuous fact that with the exception of a few horticulturally important ferns, the ecology of tropical primitive plants is essentially unknown. I can find no studies of the growth rates, competitive interactions, nutritional requirements, reproductive strategies, or population structures of tropical lichens, mosses, cycads, *Lycopodium*, *Selaginella*, fungi, or most ferns. There is, however, another reason for directing the discussion toward angiosperms. Despite the impression that might be gained by the small number of pages devoted to them in even the best modern botany texts, angiosperms are without doubt the most important green plants in contemporary tropical plant communities. I must hasten to add, however, that fungi are a notable exception. They are extremely important in litter decomposition and mycorrhizal associations. In addition, the ecological interactions among angiosperms, and among animals, angiosperms and the physical environment, account for most of the inter-habitat variation in tropical plant and animal communities. Of course, this is undoubtedly true in much of the temperate zone as well; Britain may contain more species of lichens than higher plants, but ecologically lichens are hardly more than intricate scum on the surface of the rock and tree surfaces that are too harsh for angiosperms.

While we are dealing here with the biology of the plants growing between the Tropic of Cancer and the Tropic of Capricorn, we must be constantly aware of the fact that this geographic region contains more kinds of habitats than do the mid-latitude zones. It is nearly impossible to make generalizations about tropical plant biology that will be true over large areas yet are precise enough to be of use in a specific area; the statement that epiphytes are very abundant in a tropical rainforest no more applies to a tropical deciduous forest 80 kilometres away than it does to a beach-maple forest in the northern United States. While a tropical deciduous forest may have ten times as many species of pollinating bees as an English meadow, the English meadow has ten times as many species of bees as the dwarfed forest at 3000 metre elevation on a Costa Rican mountain only 48 kilometres from the deciduous forest. The residents of San José, in Costa Rica, have names for at least eight seasons and even recognize variations on these. We stand outside the tropics looking in, and unfortunately tend to lump this diversity under one word. An additional etymological problem is that the geographer, agriculturalist, forester, entomologist, esoteric ecologist, etc., all wish to define and arrange habitats in ways that will highlight the phenomena important to their own investigations. There is no universally applicable classification of tropical climates and habitats which will serve as an optimal conceptual and etymological framework for all facets of biology.

I have constructed this book with one major goal. I wish to encourage tropical biologists to shed their white lab coats and £20 000 centrifuges and start looking at plants as dynamic, intricate and evolving creatures. The next major steps to be taken in tropical plant biology require little more than time in the field, permanence at a site, a notebook, hand counter, pruning shears, and an eye for manipulation of living systems. There is a very dangerous tendency to rely on condensations of a widely scattered literature for 'authoritative' statements about the tropics and the reader is strongly encouraged to consult the referenced studies, and to develop his own understanding of the issues and the attempts at their resolution.

The arrangement of topics in this book is only one of many possible organizations for the material at hand. Ecological relationships are reticulate rather than linear, and this is most conspicuous in the tropics, so rich in interactions. For example, the reader may find it both rewarding and frustrating to attempt to collate the material presented here among a different set of categories, such as competition, mutualism, predation, etc. May I also suggest that the reader not be dismayed by a terminology that might best be termed evolutionary shorthand. The statement '...it is likely that heavy investment in chemical protection of their few leaves is worthwhile,' may be transliterated to read, 'Those mutant genotypes that produce toxic foliage with resources that are used for other processes in the original genotype have a higher relative fitness in plants with small leaf crops than in those with large ones.'

1975   D.H.J.

Contents

1 Vegetative Biology

1.1 Introduction

The vegetative parts of a tropical plant, just as with a temperate zone plant, are primarily adaptive in the context of gathering, storage, and manipulation of resources. These activities are carried out in an environment rich in competitors, mutualists, herbivores, and variation in weather and soil. For example, most lowland tropical plants compete with individuals of other species and of many other life forms; most temperate zone plants have one or more conspecifics as nearest neighbours and the life forms of competitors are very monotonous. A number of tropical plants have mutualistic associations with ants, and the roots of many tropical plants have mutualistic mycorrhizal associations with fungi. Obligatory mutualistic associations with ants are absent from the temperate zones and while mycorrhizal associations occur, they are rarer. The tropical plant usually exists in a habitat that is far richer in species of herbivores and kinds of herbivory than that of the temperate zone plant. Within tropical habitats, the plant has to contend with mineral-poor soil and fluctuations in available water; important temperature change occurs within the 24-hour cycle and along elevational gradients. The mid-latitude counterpart often has mineral-rich soil and large fluctuations in temperature on a seasonal scale.

In tropical latitudes, there is a blurring of the distinction between the classical categories of plant vegetative-morphology-behaviour. For example, in the same habitat there are tree species that are totally deciduous during a six-month dry season, species that are completely evergreen, and species that drop their leaves in the rainy season and bear them during the dry season. In a 100 metre^2 area, life forms may range from vines to scandent shrubs, sprawling shrubs, upright shrubs, and small trees; some plants will start as shrubs and later turn into vines, and some vines become shrubs if deprived of support to climb. There are 'annual' plants whose 'year' is 40 years long (e.g., sisal, *Agave*), annual plants that grow a woody stem in less than a year, trees with a height increment of 4 metres a year and almost no woody tissue (e.g., papaya, *Carica*), and epiphytic herbs that live for tens of years without becoming woody. On the other hand, there are also habitats, such as mangrove swamps or high elevation oak forest where almost every plant is of the same life form.

Not only are there many behavioural and morphological life

(a)

(b)

(c)

Plate 1 (**a**) The leaves from the first 18 species of large shrubs and tree saplings encountered in a haphazard transect in undisturbed rainforest understory. (**b**) and (**c**) The leaves from the first 31 species of large plants encountered in a haphazard transect in three-year-old secondary succession 100 metres from the collection site of the leaves in (**a**) (Finca La Selva, Puerto Viejo, Heredia Prov., Costa Rica. July 1973).

forms within the tropics but, in addition, their proportional representation among the plant biomass and species changes from habitat to habitat. Vines disappear at high elevations, deciduous trees are rare on very poor soils, shrubs are rare in the understory of rainforest, epiphytes are rare in certain deciduous forests, and so on. Sometimes these changes mimic those encountered in moving from the tropics to the mid-latitudes (e.g., vines are also a trivial portion of the species and biomass of northern forests) but the ecological causes may be unrelated.

Only a few aspects of the vegetative morphology and behaviour of tropical trees have been chosen for discussion here. They were selected because a little is known about them or because they seem extraordinarily fertile areas for field research of the type that can be conducted on a miniscule budget.

1.2 Deciduous behaviour

Why do tropical trees discard their leaves at all? Why are they discarded at certain times and replaced at certain times? Generally, leaf drop is a response to (a) increased shading associated with competition within and between crowns, (b) damage caused by herbivores, wind or falling debris, or (c) dry weather.

In evergreen tropical habitats, the light falling on a leaf is reduced both when more leaves are added overhead in the same crown and when other crowns grow over the leaf. Leaf drop as a consequence of competition inside a crown is conspicuous in the tropics in fully insolated early successional vegetation. Here, where light is super-abundant and there is a premium on rapid vertical growth, leaves tend to be shed almost as soon as a shadow is cast on them. If minerals can be thoroughly extracted from leaves before discarding (or if the soil is rich in minerals), the cellulose skeleton that is lost means relatively little to the plant in a light-rich habitat. The lower leaves also provide attachment points for climbing vines, and so are in fact a strategic liability.

The monolayer crowns thus produced (e.g., *Cecropia*, *Macaranga*, *Ochroma*, *Piper*) are also encountered in the deep shade of evergreen forest understory. Here, monolayer crowns occur on saplings of overstory trees and on those species that attain reproductive maturity in the shade. In this nutrient- and light-poor habitat, the plant probably maintains only the most efficient leaves. However, it should also be very slow to drop one leaf and replace it, as the plant is either adapted to the low light intensity (an understory species) or 'waiting' for the sudden increase in light following a mature tree fall; in this heavily shaded circumstance, rapid vertical growth is less important

(a)

(b)   (c)

Plate 2 (a) Tropical forest in the rainy season on foothills north of Tehuantepec, Oaxaca, Mexico. Juvenile columnar cacti grow well in the full insolation received when the trees are deciduous in the dry season; this is one of the few habitats where cacti can compete well with large leafy plants. (b) A representative rainforest tree with the rainforest recently removed (near San Miguel, Heredia Prov., Costa Rica); note irregular crown that once fit in with other crowns in the canopy. (c) Result of defoliation of a *Spondias* branch by Lepidoptera larvae early in the rainy season, leading to secondary production of leaves after the caterpillars have pupated (Alajuela, Costa Rica, late June 1973).

compared to the mineral and cellulose losses that occur when a leaf is replaced. In the understory habitat, it is therefore to be expected that natural selection influences the production of leaves that are especially resistant to herbivore and mechanical damage, and to the accumulation of epiphyllae. Without these three challenges, there is no obvious reason why an understory leaf should not live for many years (as indeed do the 3–7-year-old leaves of ericaceous evergreen shrubs in the understory of deciduous forests in the south-eastern United States). The phenomenon of epiphyllous plants (e.g., algae, lichens) accumulating on the horizontal leaves of rainforest understory plants is just a special case of inter-crown competition for light.

Inter-crown competition is of course a major aspect of the life of both juvenile and mature plants. When a juvenile is 'jockeying' for position in the canopy, leaf loss and replacement in almost all of the crown occurs in order to generate an optimal crown shape. Once established, however, it is probably only the crown margins which lose some leaves through shading. Again, this is a situation where, except for herbivore and mechanical damage, evergreen tropical leaves might be expected to live a very long time. Some overstory leaves last from less than a year to at least 3 years, but virtually nothing is known of the patterns of loss within the crown nor the causes for discarding leaves. It is known that there is great inter-specific variation in tolerance to shading by tropical tree leaves. One way this is expressed is by the commonly encountered inter-specific overlapping of tree crowns and the very graphic failure to overlap when two crowns of the same species happen to be side by side (they both have the same degree of shade intolerance). The multitude of shades of green encountered in tropical forest tree leaves is likewise probably associated with a wide range of shading tolerances.

Despite the observation that there is no conspicuous physiological reason for a mature tree in evergreen tropical forest to discard and replace most of its leaves, many do so. Cordia alliodora, a canopy-member tree, may be seen standing leafless for weeks in the middle of the rainy season in a Costa Rican rainforest that receives over 4 metres of rain evenly distributed through the year. High elevation Costa Rican oaks (Quercus) may be seen to drop their entire leaf crop and then within a few days to be covered with a crop of new bright red leaves. Bright 'flushes' of pink, pale green, white or other oddly coloured new leaves can be seen dotting the upper surface of rainforest tree crowns at almost any time of year. It may be that the synchronization of entire crowns and entire populations, and the sudden protection of a small number of leaves in one cluster in one crown, are ways of escaping from herbivores. Otherwise, the herbivore population could easily build up on the new leaves if they were produced at a rate of a few per day over a long time. It is also possible that leaf replacement in established crowns is necessary owing to accumulated herbivore and wind damage. Unfortunately, nothing is known of how much damage, and of which types a leaf can sustain before it is 'economic' to replace it with a new one. This may be a similar situation to that observed when comparing evergreen and deciduous species in tropical deciduous forest; the very durable leaf may last longer, but 'costs' more initially and is less efficient photosynthetically than the flimsy leaf. In evergreen tropical forests that are species rich, we should expect to find species at each of many points along the gradient between these two extremes.

In the progression from evergreen rainforest to habitats with long and thorough dry seasons (most of the lowland tropics are seasonal with respect to rainfall), the proportion of deciduous trees and species in the canopy overstory increases. In lowland habitats with more than four rainless months, almost all of the upland trees are leafless during most of the dry season (though both wind-free or upper elevation habitats require more dry weather for the same degree of leaf loss). However, if less than about 1·5 metres of rain falls in the wet season or if the soil fertility is very low, many lowland species remain evergreen throughout the year, leaf sizes decline, and stem-photosynthesizers (e.g., Cactaceae, Euphorbiaceae) become abundant.

Along watercourses in deciduous tropical forests, many of the woody plants retain their leaves during the dry season. Some of these belong to species that are deciduous on the dry hillside and evergreen when growing along the river, but other species are evergreen in either habitat. For example, in Costa Rica some of the evergreen tree species, such as *Hymenaea courbaril*, *Manilkara chicle*, *Curatella americana*, *Andira enermis*, *Trichilia* sp., and *Ficus* spp., synchronously dehisce their entire leaf crop during the middle or late dry season and then within a week or two produce another crop of equally drought-resistant leaves. Others, such as *Byrsonima crassifolia*, the palm *Acrocomia vinifera*, and the oak *Quercus oleoides* produce new leaves during much of the year.

The leaves of tropical plants that retain their leaves during most or all of the dry season are quite different from those of plants that have leaves only during the rainy season. Evergreen leaves are small (rarely more than about 6 centimetres long and 4 centimetres wide), leathery, simple, comparatively free of insect damage, and rich in secondary compounds. The latter trait is not surprising because in the tropical dry season, the herbivorous animals are active until they run out of food. Furthermore, the shade cast by evergreen trees on hillsides and river bottoms is a major microhabitat in which many herbivorous invertebrates and vertebrates survive the dry season. The crowns of evergreen trees are much denser and more globular than those of deciduous species (which have crowns like those found on elms, oaks and maples in mid-latitude forests), and they cast much heavier shade. During the rainy season, with its lower light intensity owing to cloudy weather, this may result in sub-optimal efficiency by the lower leaves in the crown. During the dry season, however, the very intense and unobstructed sunlight undoubtedly penetrates more deeply into the crown. In addition, a deep crown receives light laterally through the crowns of adjacent leafless trees. *Jacquinia pungens*, an understory small tree in Central American deciduous forest, has carried this behaviour to an extreme. During the rainy season it is leafless. During the dry season its dense and multi-branched crown bears thousands of small, leathery and very poisonous leaves. It has no surface roots but an extremely deep tap root. *J. pungens* lives in a seasonally available desert.

Even those trees in habitats with a predictable dry season may be damaged by dry weather. If the dry season is exceptionally dry, an evergreen tree such as *Hymenaea courbaril* produces undersized leaves, presumably because not enough moisture is available for their full expansion when young. As a consequence, it probably suffers sub-optimal photosynthesis during the following year. If the rainy season starts and then stops for 4 to 6 weeks, as it did in 1971 in Guanacaste Province, Costa Rica, deciduous tree species often lose their new leaf crop, suffer severe branch mortality, and then may not bear seeds for as long as 3 years (e.g., as did *Bombacopsis quinata, Ceiba pentandra, Enterolobium cyclocarpum, Pithecellobium saman, Tabebuia rosea*). This same drought caused all the *Hymenaea courbaril* to abort their fruit crops. This behaviour by *H. courbaril* underlines the concept that it is not the dry weather *per se*, but rather the energy loss from failure of photosynthesis, that is detrimental.

The observations above suggest intriguing complications when there are two similar and intense dry seasons each year (as in Colombia on the equator). Here, the deciduous species cannot be expected to produce two separate leaf crops (one for each rainy season) since the 'return' would probably not repay the original 'investment'. It is possible that the plants have to develop a more drought-resistant leaf so as to be evergreen during at least one of the dry seasons. Such a plant should have a lower net productivity than would a deciduous species in an area with one long dry season. Furthermore, certain strategies appear unavailable to such a plant. For example, it might have difficulty setting fruits in one dry season and then retaining them for a full year before maturing them, a feature that is common among trees at higher tropical latitudes (e.g., *Cassia grandis, Enterolobium cyclocarpum, Hymenaea courbaril, Swietenia macrophylla*).

Synchrony in discarding leaves may be a simple outcome of at least three processes. First, many deciduous trees in the tropical forest may find that leaf retention is uneconomical at about the same degree of environmental dryness; this kind of synchrony should be strongly disrupted by local differences in drainage, wind exposure, soil fertility, and plant health. Second, as the various species become deciduous as the dry season approaches, any one tree need not retain its own leaves for 'ownership' of its crown space. Third, as the green foliage begins to disappear from the community, those species lacking exceptional herbivore defences will most probably receive exceptionally heavy damage to their remaining leaves. This third process leads to the intriguing question of why plants actively discard old leaves instead of simply allowing them to be eaten off. The answer must be that when a leaf is discarded, the plant has the chance to extract all possible nutrients from it. Synchrony of leaf production at the crown, population and community levels involves the inverse of these three processes.

1.3   Vines

Plants that use other plants for support and have elongate stems that invade other crowns, hereafter called 'vines' (= herbaceous and woody lianes), are the most poorly understood of all the major tropical angiosperm life forms. Though a woody vine may bear a crown as extensive as that of a large tree, vines have no commercially important wood (except for rattan palms) and thus have been of little interest to foresters. The reproductive biology of vines as a group is not unusual and thus they have escaped the attention of more esoteric biologists. For unexplained reasons, they constitute a trivial portion of temperate zone vegetation both in species and biomass. However, lowland tropical vegetation often abounds in vines. As vines rely on a rapid rate of elongation for their competitive advantage, they grow well in tropical habitats except where it is very dry or cool, or where the soil is very poor. Almost every habitat is distinguishable by the traits of its array of vines. Here, two rather different habitats will be discussed, but all tropical habitats need analysis of their vines for these and other traits.

1.3.1   Early secondary succession in deciduous forest

In old fields, riversides, roadsides, swamp edges, landslide edges, etc., vines are prominent in the dry tropics. They grow rapidly during the rainy season and, with the exception of a few evergreen Bignoniaceae, are mostly deciduous. They are perennial and capable of rapid regeneration from cutting- and fire-resistant root stocks, and many of the species persist throughout many successional stages and develop long woody stems. Most belong to the Apocynaceae, Aristolochiaceae, Asclepiadaceae, Bignoniaceae, Convolvulaceae, Dioscoreaceae, Euphorbiaceae, Fabaceae, Sapindaceae, and Vitaceae, families that are not well represented in temperate zone floras. When these families do occur at mid-latitudes, such as Fabaceae, Asclepiadaceae and Apocynaceae, most of the representatives are not vines. Tropical vines have crowns that rapidly and frequently shift location as they grow. The branches climb by twining, recurved hooks and many forms of tendrils (which commonly are modified leaves or leaflets). The leaves are often widely spaced along the branch and may form a close-fitting monolayer 'crown' over the substrate. When there is a shortage of substrate, they often climb on each other and disrupt the neat leaf arrangements encountered when inter-crown competition is less intense. Among the Fabaceae, there are even species that climb while deciduous; they move themselves well over the substrate plant's crown before producing leaves. They have only tiny leaves on the rapidly elongating branch and develop a leafy crown when the rains come.

Nutrient storage for sexual reproduction and production of new leaves is commonly accomplished with swellings of the roots and, in some cases, really large tubers. Sweet potatoes (*Ipomoea*) and yams (*Dioscorea*) are familiar examples. Presumably, the above-ground portion of the stem does not have an adequate volume for storage needs. In addition to being below the ground, tubers are generally well protected with chemical defences (see Chapter 4). They are found above ground only in habitats that lack a large biomass of animals (e.g., forests on white sand soil, forests at high elevations, and island vegetation).

Most species of vines in deciduous forest seem to adopt one of two different methods of crown production. Some have a few elongating branches that move far from the root stock before bifurcating to form a distinct crown (if they ever do). These species commonly have only a few chemically very well protected shoot tips, lose few shoot tips to herbivorous insects, and elongate relatively slowly. More commonly, vines produce many rapidly elongating branches close to the root crown. Many of these branch ends are eaten by herbivores before they grow more than a few metres. The former life form produces very diffuse crowns and is most abundant in areas that are infrequently disturbed; the latter life form produces very dense crowns and some such species may survive even if the area is cut or burned more than once per year.

Even the minute details of climbing can be of biological significance. A population of vines generally contains both right- and left-handed individuals with respect to the way they twine around the substrate;

in the northern hemisphere left-handed individuals have significantly larger seed crops than right-handed ones, and the effect is reversed in the southern hemisphere. Other 'handed' plants, such as coconuts, display the same phenomenon. It has been suggested that this is because the left-handed individuals have slightly more leaves exposed to the slanting sun's rays in the northern hemisphere than in the southern hemisphere.

The mechanically self-supporting plants of early secondary succession have a number of traits that minimize the chances of their being used as vine trellises. This protection can be most clearly demonstrated when a plant's vine defences are experimentally removed. For example, this occurs when the obligate acacia-ants are removed from a swollen-thorn acacia. These ants live in the thorns and kill any vine that starts to climb on the acacia. The acacia has many lateral branches at all heights, thorns and leaves angling upward from the branches, and compound leaves. The acacias without their ants rapidly become covered with vines while other species of self-supporting woody plants a few metres away are usually quite free of them. These other plants have smooth stems, downward pointing petioles bearing simple lanceolate leaves, and very few lateral branches within a metre of the central shoot tip. When a vine tendril or shoot tip contacts such stems, it often slides off. This leads to a mass of vines at the stem base. The shrubby acacia has a life form normally associated with more xeric habitats (that are relatively vine-free). It is of interest that where rivers run through relatively dry deciduous tropical forest, dry forest species with a shrubby life form occur near the river. While such a shrub grows very well, it often becomes a superb vine trellis and does not reach reproductive maturity owing to the inability of its crown to repel vines. Such an array of plants is an obvious candidate for some elegant experimentation.

1.3.2   Undisturbed evergreen rainforest

In the understory of evergreen rainforest on lateritic or on even better soils, woody vine stems up to 20 centimetres in diameter are a prominent part of the scenery. Free of leaves and low branches, they are the pipelines to crowns that may be nearly as large as the tree crowns that support them. A cross section of these stems shows them to consist almost entirely of water-conducting elements of very large diameter. Owing to the lack of wood deposition, they are impossible to age but it is clear from their population structure and physical locations that they are of ages equalling those of the trees that support them. Since they sprout readily from lateral roots (see section 1.4), the lineage represented by a plant may be even much older than its support. A crown of one of these vines appears to be quite dynamic in location and may be as much as 100 metres from its roots. If one follows the stem out from the first point of connection with the ground, it may amble for a hundred metres or more across and through the litter, and be connected to other large stems reaching the canopy at 40 to 50 metres height. (Incidentally, this suggests that a vine has no chance of its roots recovering nutrients that are lost when it discards its leaves.) The arboreal stems may also loop from the canopy to the ground and back up, indicating that a tree fell out from under the stem long ago. By examining tree falls of various ages, all stages of a vine's growth strategy can be encountered, since new vertical shoots most commonly become established at such sites. When trees are felled, vines may even prevent the fall of a tree that has been cut at the base, owing to cross connections with other trees. Vine crowns blend in with the tree crowns to produce a more complete canopy than do the trees alone, and appear to have leaf exchange, branch development and sexual behaviour like that of the trees. In contrast with the vines of deciduous forest, many rainforest vines do not appear to have large storage tubers as mature plants. However, like forest trees, their root systems are essentially unknown.

Recruitment by the vine population is quite complex. In addition to the vegetative 'reproduction' to be discussed in section 1.4, they produce both large and small seeds, as do the trees. Behaviourally, the seedlings are quite different from tree seedlings. Some produce small understory shrubs that appear to be quite inactive for undetermined but long periods. During this time, a large tuber is growing on the tap root. Quite suddenly, the central axis begins to elongate rapidly, at a rate of as much as 5 centimetres per day. This rapidly climbing stem has very few leaves and if substrates are available, may climb at least 5 metres and probably much more without proliferating into the beginnings of a crown. During the period of intensive growth, the tuber becomes very soft and presumably exhausted of stored nutrients. In a habitat that contains very little sunlight for photosynthesizing, such a growth strategy is a way of attaining a high level in the forest while minimizing the amount of time that the succulent shoot tip is available to herbivores. A quite different set of species of vines simply start out as rapidly growing vine seedlings. They usually grow from seeds weighing as much as 20 grammes, and are nearly leafless for many metres. They put all their energy into vertical growth. For example, if growing in a dark room near a well lit window, a *Dioclea macrocarpa* seedling will grow past the window until it hits the ceiling, and only then turn back and try to grow out the window. Almost every 'young' vine of any size will be found to be connected by a lateral root to an established vine or root.

1.4   Vegetative reproduction

The growth patterns of tropical perennial plants suggest an intriguing problem and severely inadequate terminology with respect to the concept of 'vegetative reproduction'. Apomixis and other forms of asexual production of dispersable propagules do occur in the tropics, but the most conspicuous form of asexual multiplication is the production of long horizontal roots just below the soil surface, which in turn produce vertical shoots from some nodes. Sloppily called 'vegetative reproduction', we only apply this term because we cannot see underground. Such a plant is hardly doing more than producing a diffuse crown. At first, the new shoots are drawing on the established plant crown just as are the new branches that are produced in an arboreal crown when the rainy season starts. Even when the connection to the shoot is severed by herbivores or by the 'parent', this should not be regarded as an act of reproduction. The new shoot is no more the unit of selection than is a leaf in a tree crown. Evolutionarily, this type of growth should be viewed as a class of resource allocation whereby an established plant becomes huge and is not restricted to the location of the original seedling. Forest vines provide some of the best examples of this behaviour. If a habitat is populated by a large number of individuals produced asexually from one parent, and an event occurs that leads to differential mortality among them, it is directly analogous to predation on part of the worker ants in a colony, or to differential branch death owing to herbivory in a tree crown. Hard as it is to visualize, we may be dealing with the situation where the true reproductive population of a plant may be an extraordinarily small number of individuals, each of which is very large, perhaps numerously subdivided, and spread over many hectares.

The interesting question then is 'why is this form of crown expansion so abundant in the tropics?' A few answers may be formulated, but our knowledge of the biology of tropical wild plants is so primitive that they must at best be viewed as halting first steps.

First, year-round warm weather permits this behaviour. The new sucker shoot has the resources of the established plant to draw on rather than being confined to the small reserves that can be placed in a seed. It may continue to grow (and compete) well into the dry season and therefore this type of crown expansion can be used at almost any time of the year. In contrast, seedlings are much more restricted in the times at which they have any chance of survival. For example, if a patch of deciduous forest is cut during the late rainy season, many of the old root stocks immediately put up vigorous sucker shoots that grow and remain leafy throughout the dry season, while nearby adults of the same species are leafless and seedlings are dying of desiccation. Even without cutting, the arboreal sucker shoots from horizontal subterranean roots may retain their leaves in the dry season while the established plant loses its leaves.

Second, a species-rich area of vegetation usually contains many diverse life forms and therefore may exhibit different kinds of competitive weakness. A plant may well be able to expand its crown more readily at various (and unpredictable) distances from the established crown than on the edge of the crown itself, as for example, when it is adjacent to particularly dangerous competitors or is being overtopped by a vine. In an environment containing highly heterogeneous resources, subdivision may be appropriate for a sedentary organism.

Third, in habitats where seedling establishment is extremely difficult, we may expect strong selection for great adult longevity and great adult size; generally, a plant with double the volume of canopy produces much more than a double-size seed crop. A plant may have to be huge before it can produce enough seeds to have the chance to make even one new reproductive adult. Once a tree is established, it may well be highly adapted to put part of its resources into sucker shoots rather than seeds, in order to increase both seed crop size and plant longevity. This selective pressure would, of course, become progressively weaker the greater the nutritional drain on the established plant of getting a sucker shoot to reproductive size. It is therefore not surprising to find that rainforest trees do not readily produce sucker shoots from stumps or roots, while rainforest vines and almost all woody plants of deciduous forest display this behaviour.

Some methodological comments can now be made. First, in habitats that man frequently burns, cuts, or grazes (but where roots are left intact), plants that root and stump sprout are more likely to survive. Since most of the easily accessible tropics are of this type, one can be quickly left with the illusion that all tropical plants do this all the time. This is clearly not the case in more natural circumstances, but we know so little about natural vegetation that it is hard to know how badly our view is distorted. The natural circumstances are of greatest importance in that they give us some idea of the selective pressures that led to the evolution of 'vegetative reproduction'. Second, to understand the phenomenon, we need some straightforward physiological descriptions of what stimulates a plant to produce sucker shoots at a particular time, and what prevents further resources from being put into a sucker shoot that is losing in competition or dying from herbivory.

1.5 Epiphytes

While conspicuously absent from the branches of mid-latitude forest trees (with the exception of the bromeliad Spanish 'moss' (*Tillandsia ustinoides*) in the southern United States), small angiosperm herbs and shrubs growing epiphytically on tree crowns and trunks are a prominent portion of the biomass and even the species list of some tropical habitats. They are accompanied by ferns and a wide variety of primitive plants; only the latter groups do well in the temperate zones as epiphytes. In all but the very driest tropical habitats there are a few angiosperm epiphytes, but their biomass is greatest at upper intermediate to high elevations, where clouds press against the mountains most of the day, and they are most species-rich in low intermediate elevation rainforest with a mild dry season. The primary families are Gesneriaceae, Melastomataceae, Cactaceae, Rubiaceae, Asclepiadaceae, Solanaceae, Bromeliaceae, and Orchidaceae. The latter two families are almost entirely epiphytic and contain most of the angiosperm epiphytes in the Neotropics. Terrestrial (non-epiphytic) Bromeliaceae live mostly in xeric and very high elevation sites, and terrestrial orchids are high elevation and mid-latitude in distribution. Somewhat enigmatically, Bromeliaceae are absent from the Old World tropics; while various Old World ferns appear to be morphological analogues to bromeliads, there appears to be a very large amount of empty branch habitat. One hesitates, however, to suggest the obvious experiment of introducing bromeliads to the Old World because of the strong possibility of economic repercussion.

Clearly, the angiosperm epiphytic life form has evolved many times. Ecologically, an epiphyte is a perennial plant which does not have to produce and maintain massive woody stems and branches. However, it has to contend with an extremely nutrient-poor substrate (the roots are dependent on rain water, a small amount of litter fall, and material brought by animals) and a very erratic water supply (soaked when it rains, the plant lives in a desert when the wind blows). While the epiphyte's habitat is on average better insolated than is the forest floor, an individual epiphyte has little chance to shift its crown to avoid shading. On the other hand, once established on a branch, the chances are reduced of another plant growing up next to the adult epiphyte, if for no other reason than substrate is missing from most of its periphery.

The competitive interactions of epiphytes are complex, but probably amenable to analysis. C. Schnell, working with Central American epiphytes, finds that in habitats with up to 10 to 20 epiphyte species in at least three families, relatively distinct portions of the habitat can be identified for each species by recording the following kinds of simple parameters for each individual epiphyte: distance from the tree centre, height above ground, depth in the tree crown, distance to nearest conspecific, degree of shading of the branch, and angle of the supporting branch. Most species of epiphytes produce very large numbers of very small and wind-dispersed seeds. Their successful germination and growth on a tree branch appears to be strongly influenced by competitors and the physical environment (as well as by mycorrhizal associations in some cases). In contrast to many other tropical associations of plants, it appears that epiphyte community structure may be little influenced by herbivory.

Epiphyte leaves are conspicuously much more evergreen than those of the plants on which they grow, apparently very desiccation resistant, and quite free from herbivore damage. In view of the nutrient-poor environment of epiphytes, it is likely that heavy investment in chemical defences of their few leaves is worthwhile (see Chapter 4). Like vines, most epiphytes are impossible to age because they do not lay down woody tissue. However, their very slow growth rate suggests that they live for tens of years. There are some individual bromeliads and orchids in Costa Rica that do not appear to have changed in size in the past ten years. They flower every year and as new leaves and short stems are added, the old ones rot off. Unless the branch falls off, there is no obvious reason why an angiosperm epiphyte should die once established, except through competition for light and exceptionally severe fluctuations in the physical environment.

1.6   Roots

In a system where most of the inorganic nutrients are in the living vegetation, it is not surprising to find that the roots compete strongly with the fungi, bacteria and litter animals for newly fallen litter. Inorganic material that finds its way to the soil is likely to be rapidly lost by leaching during the heavy rains of the rainy season. It is also not surprising to find that in such a system the roots are often involved in a mutualistic interaction with fungi that appear to be specialists at gathering minerals. Current studies in Costa Rican rainforest by D. Janos suggest that many rainforest tree roots may have virtually no root hairs, and depend entirely on mycorrhizal fungi for mineral uptake. The tree apparently provides carbohydrates to the fungus, which are taken up by the hyphae penetrating the roots, and the fungus moves minerals into the roots from its hyphae in the soil and litter. It may be significant that such associations seem to be best developed on tropical white sand soils (which have almost no physiologically useful minerals) and among epiphytic orchids, and to be most poorly developed in plants of early primary succession (e.g., *Cecropia*, *Ochroma*, *Trema*, *Urera*) that normally grow on soils enriched from fire ash, flood water soil deposition, or litter from a fallen tree.

2 Pollination Biology

2.1 Introduction

From the animal's viewpoint, pollination is an incidental by-product of the harvest of a widely scattered resource (pollen and/or nectar) that comes in diverse containers called flowers. An animal that is harvesting pollen and/or nectar (= flower visitor) is by no means guaranteed to be an efficient pollinator, if indeed it is a pollinator at all. From the plant's viewpoint, pollination is an exercise in optimizing the flow of genes to other flowers and the receipt of genes from an optimal number of other plants. This process is not synonymous with pollination, though it is obviously related. Unfortunately, pollen flow is not synonymous with gene flow and the relationship is unclear in the tropics just as it is with most mid-latitude plants. Optimization of gene flow generally involves attracting and feeding certain animals, contaminating these animals with pollen, repelling or avoiding other animals, and doing all three at a minimal overall cost per unit of genetic information transferred at the best time to the best place. There is no altruistic behaviour on the part of either the plant or the animal.

The tropics contain some very complex examples of integration of the needs of the flower visitor with those of the flower, but such complexities are by no means limited to the tropics. For example, the arid and semi-arid regions just outside the tropics have the greatest species richness of bees of any part of the world. However, the array of flower visitors and pollinators in the tropics is richer in species than in most mid-latitude habitats. In the tropics, flower visiting is spread much more evenly over the major animal taxa, with bats, birds, moths, butterflies, flies, wasps and bees all being important and often one of them will be the only pollinator.

From the viewpoint of the plant, pollination biology in the tropics does not differ in any significant qualitative manner from that of the mid-latitudes. However, certain portions of the overall system receive very different emphasis from their mid-latitude counterparts. Some of the noteworthy examples are:

(1) low proportion of wind-pollinated plants,
(2) high proportion of vertebrates acting as pollinators,
(3) high proportion of social bees as visitors to flowers (and perhaps acting as pollinators),
(4) long distance between conspecific individuals of obligatorily outcrossed plants,

(5) large number of complex relationships between particular pollinators and particular plants, and
(6) complex patterns of flowering synchrony.

2.2   Low proportion of wind-pollinated plants

With the exception of wind-pollinated grasses and sedges in savannahs, marshes and other windy habitats (where plants occur in very low diversity patches), animal transport of pollen is the rule in the tropics. Without doubt, the primary selective pressure generating this pattern is the fact that conspecific individuals of tropical plants usually have one or more plants of other species between them (see section 2.4). Wind is a very poor carrier of pollen in quantities adequate for pollination, unless the donors are immediately adjacent to the recipient and absolute distances between plants are short. Lack of wind is not a major problem in the canopy, irrespective of the height of the canopy above the ground. Even in rainforests there are many species of tropical plants with wind-dispersed seeds, and air over all tropical vegetation types is generally turbulent. A second major factor in animal pollination is that the tropical dry season does not necessarily inhibit (poikilotherm) insect activity, as does the cool weather of the temperate zone early spring and autumn. Desiccation is the major problem encountered by animals active in the dry season. This can be partly overcome by harvesting nectar in flowers, and gathering moisture becomes a major reason for animals to visit flowers.

The understory of evergreen forest is the one major tropical habitat where a lack of wind might be a primary cause of the lack of wind pollination. Understory grasses are sometimes pollinated by insects, as are the palms, which were long thought of as wind-pollinated. Other rainforest monocots such as gingers, bromeliads, orchids, and bananas have species that are pollinated by either bats, birds or insects. This is the case even when they are species that regularly grow in monospecific clumps, such as the neotropical banana-like *Heliconia* and *Calathea*. Even when there are pure stands of one species of tree, as in coastal mangrove swamps or in early succession, wind is not the pollen vector for tropical trees.

The absence of wind pollination means that there is a large array of animals supported by the plant community's flower production, rather than flower production supporting the litter micro-organisms that live off wind-borne pollen in mid-latitude forests. Pollination by animals may also result in a larger portion of the primary productivity going into pollination costs in the tropics than in mid-latitudes. While we have no data on this point, it seems a reasonable hypothesis because where conspecific plants are close together, but both winds and animals are available, selection has frequently resulted in wind-pollinated systems. Tropical savannah grasses and mid-latitude forest trees are two examples.

2.3   Large number of vertebrates as pollinators

Many tropical plants are co-evolved with bats and birds as pollinators. The exclusively New World hummingbirds (Trochilidae) comprise over 300 species and are almost entirely tropical. They are the only pollinators of thousands of species of plants. The honeyeaters (Meliphagidae) form a parallel case in the Old World tropics, though the flowers may not be so obligatorily tied to them, nor they to the flowers. A large proportion of the increase in number of mammal species, in moving from North America into the neotropics, is due to the appearance of nectarivorous and frugivorous bats. We may legitimately ask what difference does it make to the plant if it is pollinated by a vertebrate rather than by an insect.

At the trivial level, it is obvious that each group of vertebrates is associated with a set of individual flower traits. Hummingbird flowers are usually tubular, red to orange, and exposed on the surface of the plant crown. Bat flowers often contain copious amounts of nectar, open at night, and are large with greenish, white or purple coloration. Bat flowers are commonly on large trees or vines while hummingbird flowers are usually on herbs, vines, shrubs and small trees.

More important, plants pollinated by vertebrates tend to bear their flowers during most of the year. The year-round food needs of a vertebrate select in favour of a broad spread of flowering times of individuals within the tree crown and within the community. Associated with such a phenology, species of plants that are pollinated by vertebrates usually have only a small per cent of the total flower crop open on any given night or day. This means that a single animal is very unlikely to be satiated by one plant. A singular consequence is that we almost never observe specific, one-to-one relationships between a species of plant and a species of vertebrate pollinator. Hummingbirds and bats each are host-specific pollinators to a set of plant species, rather than any one species in the habitat. Another consequence is that the pollinator must be able to remember a complex feeding route. Finally, the spread of conspecific pollen among the population is probably increased as compared with ordinary insect pollinators, which often restrict their visits to a small array of flowers at one site. A noteworthy exception to this conclusion is the case where hummingbird-pollinated plants, such as *Heliconia* spp., happen to grow in a patch over which a male hummingbird establishes a territory. The pollen from these flowers then tends to stay in that patch, and little outside pollen will be brought in. In analysing such flower-pollinator interactions, we must always bear in mind that, unlike female bees, vertebrate pollinators are not visiting a flower to get material to carry back to a nest, but rather for fuel to carry out other tasks. However, the foraging patterns of a nesting female hummingbird may have similar constraints to those of a large female bee, who must return repeatedly to the same site.

Vertebrate pollinators may move many miles between conspecific plants. Bats are known to fly 3 to 16 kilometres in one night of foraging. Furthermore, it is almost certain that hummingbirds migrate within and between tropical habitats. For example, a major portion of a lowland hummingbird fauna may move into high tropical elevations and be very reliable pollinators for a small part of the year, in a habitat that could not support a large number of nectarivorous birds throughout the year. Even here, however, we must recognize that the apparent lack of food plants for hummingbirds at certain times of year at high elevations in the neotropics may be due solely to the fact that over evolutionary time the birds have found it more profitable to move to the lowlands and thus hummingbird flowers never evolved at high elevations during these seasons.

Vertebrate pollinators may be very destructive. Hummingbirds may not only restrict pollen flow by establishing territories in tree crowns or over clumps of herbs or vines, but the short-billed ones often puncture the bases of long tubular flowers to get nectar, thereby making the flower less attractive to the long-billed hummingbird that normally pollinates the flower, and allowing bees to get at the nectar. Bats sometimes eat whole flowers as well as pollinate them.

2.4   High proportion of social bees

A large proportion of the species and biomass of tropical bees are social. While a mid-latitude habitat generally has at best a few species of social bumblebees (though at high latitudes and at high elevations they are a major part of the flower-visitor fauna), a lowland neotropical rainforest habitat may have 10 to 20 per cent of its 200 to 300 species of bees in social genera (primarily *Trigona* and *Melipona*). In many ways, a social bee colony is like a vertebrate. It requires year-round food, exceptionally well-protected large nest sites, and large quantities of food per individual (=colony). The collective experience of its workers may even be regarded as a type of crude memory. However, from the plant's viewpoint, most of the social bees are a detrimental component in the ecosystem. They are primarily flower visitors rather than pollinators.

Associated with the necessity of finding large amounts of food throughout the year, social bees are specialists at scavenging pollen and nectar that was missed or not yet gathered by pollinators, collecting pollen from flowers that are constructed so as to allow only entry of specialist pollinators, collecting nearly all the pollen that adheres to their bodies, and adjusting the number of foraging trips to the amount of food available. They also recruit other members of the colony to a large food source, and may establish a fiercely defended territory over the food. All of these factors greatly lower the chance of social bees carrying pollen from one plant to another. However, this negative effect is less true for the large social bees (*Bombus*) than the small ones (*Trigona, Melipona*).

Within the tropics, where evergreen rainforest gives way to deciduous forest, the relative proportion of species and biomass of social bees declines. Along the same gradient the production of flowers becomes more synchronous at the community level (see section 2.7). In the deciduous forest, solitary bees, dormant in underground cells during most of the year, appear in great numbers at the time when many of the plants in the community come into flower. Social bees not only suffer extreme food shortages when the deciduous forest is undergoing vegetative growth in the rainy season, but encounter severe competition for nectar and pollen products during the dry season flowering.

On the other hand, moving up neotropical mountains, the social bumblebees (*Bombus*) become the major pollinators (along with hummingbirds), but are notorious for robbing hummingbird flowers by cutting holes in the base to get at the nectar. They, like the hummingbirds, are capable of flying at temperatures as low as 8 to 10 degrees Centigrade, and constitute a pollinator array not unlike that of the high latitudes.

2.5   Long distances between obligatorily outcrossed plants

As tropical agriculturalists have known for many years, and contemporary pollination studies with wild trees are showing, many tropical trees (and possibly other woody plants) are obligatorily outcrossed (self-sterile). Since the individuals of these plants are often fifty to several hundred metres apart in the forest, they are forced to rely on animals for pollination. This also places a heavy premium on two rather different flowering strategies.

(1) The plant may produce a large and conspicuous flower crop, the primary adaptive value of which is attraction of relatively unspecialized

pollinators that locate the plant primarily by noticing it at the time they are searching for pollen and/or nectar. Such plants characteristically produce far more flowers than they have the energy to produce seeds from, and they flower over a short time period with all the individuals in the population highly synchronized. These plants are often pollinated and visited by many species of small to medium-sized bees and a host of miscellaneous insects, with occasional visits by more specialized pollinators.

(2) The plant may produce a small and relatively inconspicuous flower crop, with flowers produced a few at a time over a long period. Such plants are generally pollinated by birds, butterflies, bats, large moths, or large bees. These animals apparently have a memory adequate for them to return to the same plants day after day. They can fly very long distances between plants (e.g., some large solitary Costa Rican bees may be able to fly as far as 22 kilometres in a feeding route). The number of flowers produced often closely matches the number of fruits produced.

Either of the above two pollination modes has the potential to yield outcrossing, provided that the plants are growing in the appropriate part of the habitat. For emergent rainforest trees, where a large flower crop will be very conspicuous, mass-flowering (the first type) may be best. For trees with crowns within the canopy, epiphytes and understory plants, the second type of flowering behaviour may often be optimal.

A recognition of these two different flowering strategies emphasizes that in many cases, the number of seeds or fruits set will not be a measure of pollination 'efficiency'. The plant makes as many seeds as its energy budget allows, and pollination efficiency has to be measured by the amount of new genetic information obtained from the pollen donors and contributed by the pollen receivers. This consideration is particularly important in the tropics, where flower crop size, timing and other traits are likely to be optimized with respect to attracting a certain set of pollinators, avoiding or repelling flower visitors, and optimizing the genetic variability in the seed crop.

2.6 Many complex interactions between particular plant species and their pollinators

The tropics have long been known for spectacular co-evolved interactions between particular pollinators and the floral morphology of their host plants. Unfortunately, attention to this gaudy, but usually trivial, aspect of the interaction has allowed us to avoid working out the complex and more difficult ecological processes that underlie the patterns described in the previous sections. Three such systems are described here, but the reader must realize that this is just the tip of the iceberg.

One of the best-known complex pollinator systems is that of the figs (*Ficus* spp.) and the *Blastophaga* solitary wasps that carry pollen from fig to fig in special pouches on the legs or body. After pollinating the flowers, the wasps oviposit in specialized sterile ovaries, leaving the fertile ovaries to develop. The larvae mature in the sterile ovaries and the emerging wasps collect pollen that is produced at this later time. The wasps then leave this ripe 'fruit' in search of other fig trees. The tiny wasp is delicate and must find another suitable fig within a few days. Furthermore, it must find another fig tree, because the figs ripen synchronously within the crown of a rainforest fig tree.

The fragility of the wasp has very interesting consequences for the population of figs in any particular area. If the population density of fig trees is high, as in a mainland rainforest, at any given time some of the trees are bearing fruits of the proper age for infestation by the wasps; in other words, there is strong selection for intra-population asynchrony. This may well have developed hand in hand with the selection for seed dispersal of figs by frugivorous birds and bats, animals that require a continuous fruit intake throughout the year owing to the low quality of their food. However, if the population density of figs is low or small in some absolute sense, as on a small island or a badly fragmented mainland habitat, there are not enough trees on average for there to be one at the right stage available at any one time. Here then, there is strong selection for fruiting asynchrony *within* the crown of any one fig tree. Not surprisingly, fig trees on small Caribbean islands and in riparian forest running through deciduous forest display just such asynchrony of fruiting time.

A second well-known complex system is that of the neotropical orchids that are obligatorily pollinated by male euglossine bees. These large bees collect and absorb (through the legs) complex organic compounds from the orchid, and, in an unknown manner, these compounds greatly increase longevity. The males have life spans as long as 3 to 6 months, which appears to be most exceptional for male bees. Of much greater ecological interest are the consequences of such a tight relationship for community structure. First, the male bees will be able to pollinate plants that occur at very low density and have great distances between conspecifics, because they so actively and accurately seek out plants in flower. Second, by being long-lived, the bees select for asynchrony of flowering. Associated with this, the female bees are also active throughout the year, and have the same effect on their host plants. To put it another way, those host plants under selection for long flowering periods for other reasons now have a long-lived pollinator with which they can co-evolve. However, if the females are to gather pollen from rare and widely dispersed plants, each with only a few flowers, they will have to gather pollen and nectar from many species. Analysis of pollen in cells, and records of flowers visited, shows that in some cases they do just this.

It should now be obvious why these bees are conspicuously absent from almost all Caribbean Islands, as are the orchids that they pollinate. This is so despite the fact that the tiny seeds of orchids must surely be blown frequently to the islands, and the bees are such strong fliers that some could probably fly there even without help from the wind. For the bees to become established the orchid has to be established and there has to be a sufficient number of hosts for the female bees. However, such a complex of plants cannot become established until the bees are established to provide them with pollinators. In short, even if we waited for many millions of years, there is no evidence that the complex of euglossine bees and their host plants would become established on the islands.

A third example, long suspected but only just now being documented by H. and I. Baker and their associates is the incorporation of significant amounts of amino acids in flower nectar. Flower-visiting insects may obtain amino acids from the flower in three ways. Well-understood is the idea that the pollen collected by adult bees and eaten by the larvae provides all life stages of the bee with amino acids. L. Gilbert has now shown that some neotropical butterflies collect pollen on their tongues, add nectar, and then drink the nectar that contains the amino acids that have been leached out of the pollen. Different species of plants have substantially different amounts of amino acids (and perhaps in different proportions) in their nectar, and the quantity is related to the type of pollinator. Thus, in the tropics, we may expect to find a higher proportion of those species that have large amounts of amino acids in their nectar, since the pollinator role is spread over a larger portion of the animal taxa than in mid-latitude habitats. While bees have a very nitrogen-rich food in that they gather pollen, if the other animals (butterflies, hummingbirds, bats, moths) are to be obligate specialists on flowers, there will be very strong selection favouring those plants that incorporate even small amounts of nitrogen in their floral nectar. The ecological implications of this last example of very tight co-evolution between flower and pollinator are very great.

2.7   Complex patterns of flowering synchrony

A conspicuous aspect of neotropical lowland forests is the major peak in flowering activity among the tree species during the dry season. There is also a peak about one month after the rains begin, a peak that is primarily made up of rare trees that have inconspicuous flowers. In sufficiently arid areas where the tree crowns are not often in direct contact, the trees remain synchronized in flowering time, but the synchronization is often related to some other season, such as the early weeks of the rainy season. Moving into rainforest from deciduous forest, the synchrony at the community level is still evident, but it is not so sharply defined and displays multiple peaks. Shrubs in the understory of rainforest have even less inter-specific synchrony of flowering times, though the shrubs of deciduous forest are highly synchronized in flowering behaviour. In aggregate, the species of herbaceous plants in areas with a well-developed dry season usually start flowering about the middle of the rainy season and are finished when it ends.

These brief generalizations allow us to focus on a core problem in tropical plant biology. It is often very difficult, but very important, to separate the cues (such as the beginning of the rainy season, or a three-week intensely dry spell) used by the plants in producing inter- and intra-population flowering synchrony, from the actual selection pressure favouring the synchronization. Many things can select for synchronization of flower crops, but the major four are probably the need for cross-pollination (intra-population synchronization), the need to flower when the majority of pollinators are active (intra-community synchronization), the need to flower and fruit at a time that minimizes the interference with competitive interactions (intra-community synchronization with the dry season), and satiation of animals that eat seeds or flowers (intra-tree, intra-population and intra-community synchronization). However, there is no physiological reason why flowering need be synchronized for fruiting synchrony.

When dealing with a community of many hundreds of species of woody plants, it is obvious that many will use different cues to achieve these timings. Small wonder that there is a high intra- and inter-specific variance about the mean of flowering time. It should be a rare event when the physical environment produces the proper cue for all the individuals of each tree species in the same year, yet is sufficiently heterogeneous as to actually provide cues. Further, with current agricultural practices greatly modifying the local physical environment in ways that will be differently perceived by each species of tree, it is almost impossible to make sense out of community-level flowering patterns in much of the contemporary tropics.

3 Fruit and Seed Biology

3.1 Introduction

The primary adaptive significance of the structures around the seed, termed here 'the fruit' for convenience, is protection and movement of the seeds. This is true in the tropics as well as at higher latitudes, but is more intricately developed in the tropics. As the bulk of tropical dicotyledonous vegetation is made up of woody plants, the following discussion is intended to apply to them. Fruit ecology of tropical terrestrial herbaceous plants is very poorly known but appears very similar to that of temperate zone herbs. This is not surprising when we consider that terrestrial herbaceous plants are prominent in the tropics only in those habitats that have conditions not unlike mid-latitude habitats rich in herbs: grasslands, mountain tops, repeatedly disturbed sites, etc.

3.2 Immature fruit

From the time of fruit set until the fruit is presented to the seed dispersal agent, seeds are conspicuous potential food for herbivorous animals in search of nutrient-rich plant tissues. With the exception of odd plants like peanuts (*Arachis*), the growing seeds (a) cannot be buried as can storage tubers, (b) cannot be incased in a hard seed coat because they must expand, (c) probably have the same difficulties with self-intoxication as would eggs if they had chemical defences within the seed tissue, (d) must occur in relatively large numbers, and (e) probably cannot reach full development very rapidly (as compared to a leaf, for example).

This great susceptibility of the growing seed to predation makes the immature fruit the primary defence. While detailed comparative analyses are almost non-existent for wild tropical fruits, the 'taste test' suggests that green fruits usually contain chemical defences similar to those of the mature leaves of the parent plant. Presumably, the secondary compounds in green fruit have the same high diversity as do the secondary compounds in tropical foliage (see Chapter 4 for a discussion of the nature of secondary compounds). These chemicals may, however, occur in greater quantities in fruits. For example, tropical trees with defensive resin in the wood and leaves often have immature fruits that exude copious quantities of resin when punctured. The green pods of the neotropical *Hymenaea courbaril* (Leguminosae) offer one example (incidentally, much of Central American amber is the fossil resin of this tree), but such a system occurs even in conifers. In the tropics, where the fruit is often destined eventually to be an edible attractant for specific dispersal agents, there is a major biochemical problem. Over a short time, the fruit must change from being toxic to edible. Except for some commercial fruits, nothing is known of the intriguing biochemistry that must occur in the myriads of tropical fruits that perform this transformation. It might be added that the similarity of green fruits to leaves does not stop with chemical defences. The photosynthate from the green fruit appears to contribute a major portion of the energy used in fruit and seed development.

Developmental timing is also a major defence for tropical immature fruits. For example, there are two distinct ripening systems conspicuous among trees in tropical deciduous forest. The majority flower and then proceed with rapid fruit development to produce mature seeds in as little as a month. Since this is often done when the tree is leafless, the tree must be using its stored reserves for fruit maturation (e.g., in Costa Rica, *Bombacopsis, Ceiba, Cassia, Pterocarpus, Cochlospermum, Gliricidia, Spondias, Tabebuia*). Here, developmental rates may approximate the maximum possible and the immature fruit is susceptible to herbivores for the minimum possible time. On the other hand, there are numerous species that delay their seed maturation for six months to a year after the flowering period. When the parent flowers in one dry season and matures its fruits during the following flowering season, the phenomenon is often overlooked. There appear to be several selective pressures that promote such behaviour. It is tempting to conclude that the tree is delaying its fruit maturation so that the seeds are available just prior to the next (second) rainy season. However, this reply leaves unanswered the question of why the tree does not mature them rapidly with reserves between the time of flowering and the immediately oncoming (first) rainy season. If we argue that the tree does not have adequate reserves to mature fruits and flower in the same season, we are left with the obvious question of why it does not store reserves from the previous season. Perhaps the tree is temporarily conserving its resources to be certain of adequate leaf and branch development after flowering, and to be certain of dry season survival. While such complex questions can also be asked of temperate zone trees, this line of inquiry appears untouched.

Among the species of tropical deciduous forest trees that delay the development of their fruits, there is a conspicuous dichotomy. On part of the trees (e.g., in Costa Rica, *Enterolobium cyclocarpum, Guazuma ulmifolia, Acacia cornigera, Cassia grandis, Pithecellobium saman*) the fruits remain tiny for many months, with full expansion occurring only during the last several months of development. Presumably the tree is putting some of its photosynthate into stored reserves during the time when the pods are small. The other tree species (e.g., *Hymenaea courbaril, Swietenia macrophylla, Lonchocarpus* sp., *Hippocratea* sp.) produce a full-sized fruit shortly after flowering. These green fruits contribute to the tree's overall energy budget, as well as continually receiving photosynthate from the rest of the tree throughout development. It is characteristic of this group that most of the abortions of immature fruit occur very early in the life of the fruit crop. In the previous group, abortions occur throughout the period that the fruit remains small.

It is likely that the primary selective force for delayed fruit expansion is the uncertainty as to which individual fruits will be lost to herbivores. For example, in a *Cassia grandis* (Leguminosae) fruit crop, as much as 75 per cent of the small green pods may be attacked by Lepidoptera larvae during the first six months of the crop's life. After this 'pruning' of the crop, the tree aborts enough healthy pods to reduce the crop to about 100 to 300 pods, and these then mature rapidly during the next six months. If the tree had started out with 300 or more rapidly enlarging pods, the energy loss to the predation by the moth larva would have been much greater.

Such delayed timings are easiest in weather sufficiently gentle that the tree can maintain actively growing tissues year round. However, it is not obvious why many mid-latitude trees cannot do the same. In fact, there are even a few conifer species that require two summers for cone development. It should always be remembered that it is unlikely that the timing of fruit maturation is required to occur at a certain time because of the timing of flowering. Behaviour of fruit maturation is an unexplored area in the tropics as well as at higher latitudes. About the best generalization that can be made is that there is a much greater range and more diverse pattern of ripening times in tropical than temperate fruits.

3.3 The mature fruit

Tropical fruits display a fantastic diversity of form, and fruiting displays a very great variety of behaviour. However, this diversity is primarily at the level of fine detail. All the broad categories of dispersal and crop maturation behaviour found in the tropics are also represented in the mid-latitudes, but in quite different proportions (which are as yet poorly documented).

'Dispersal' as a process needs a few words of explanation. Mere release of a fruit by the parent tree may well not constitute dispersal. For example, when a mangrove tree drops a fruit, it places the seed

within reach of the salt water which may float it to a suitable germination site in the mangrove swamp. In like manner, when a *Scheelea* palm
fruit drops to the ground, the fruit is placed within reach of rodents
(e.g., pacas and agoutis), which will carry some of the seeds far from
the parent tree. The seeds on the ground beneath a parent tree are
very likely to be undispersed seeds and in a certain sense, a reproductive failure by the plant. They commonly suffer extraordinarily severe
mortality at this location (see paragraph (c), below). Less easily resolved,
but equally a biological problem, is whether a seed 'dispersed' by the
wrong agent should be regarded as dispersed. Unfortunately the
problem cannot be examined in detail, as virtually nothing is known of
the fate of dispersed seed of tropical plants.

Dispersal is functional for at least three major reasons. The proportions of these three reasons differ strongly both between the tropics
and higher latitudes, and among tropical habitats.

(a) Where seedlings grow directly beneath or very near the parent,
there is a maximal chance of the seedling undergoing intense competition with a conspecific. In species-rich tropical forests (each species
represented by only a few widely scattered individuals), the seed that
germinates outside (is dispersed outside) the perimeter of the roots or
the vertical projection of the branch crown of the parent has a low
chance of being near a conspecific. Furthermore, the parent plant's
fitness is likely to be lowered if its resource base is blanketed with
conspecifics, even if they are its own juveniles. Such an act would be
even more detrimental to the tropical parent than to a parent tree in a
mid-latitude forest (which is usually growing on relatively good soil).

(b) The physical and competitive environment is likely to have
changed at the exact location of the parent plant since the time when
the parent was a seedling. Such succession may range from that on a
large scale such as when a river course changes, to a hole in the
canopy where a single tree fell. From the viewpoint of the parent plant,
the conditions maximally favourable for seedling survival occur at unpredictable distances from the parent, though not in unpredictable
sizes, patterns and numbers. Dispersal is a one-movement event,
oriented around optimizing the number of seeds placed in sites of
various 'safeness' from a physical-competitive-predator standpoint;
such a game is very intricate in complex tropical habitats, but probably differs little from the case in higher latitudes in species-poor
tropical habitats such as swamps and on very poor soil.

(c) As also discussed in Chapter 5, the parent plant and its cohorts
of undispersed juveniles provide a concentration of food for seed-
and seedling-predators. A juvenile has little chance of escape except
by dispersal from the area. This may be the most important reason for
dispersal of tropical forest trees, but is probably a less important reason

for annual and woody plants of early successional stages. This type of dispersal is made very complicated by the fact that many tropical dispersal agents are also seed predators, and a seed predator to one tree species may be a dispersal agent to another. For example, when much fruit is falling, an agouti is likely to eat the fruit and bury the seed far from the parent. However, a month later when fruit is no longer falling, it is likely to dig up the seeds and eat them.

Dispersal as a form of escape from seed predators appears to play a proportionately greater role in the tropics than in the temperate zones. The central problem is that in an area where the weather is generally favourable to animals the year around, there is only plant chemistry and dispersal behaviour as a way of escape for the plant. At mid-latitudes, the animal populations are more depressed by the weather (and lack of food) between seed crops than in the tropics. Further, outside the tropics it is physiologically much easier for synchronization to occur in a tree population or community than inside. This is because in the relatively uniform tropics, it appears difficult to come up with a supra-annual cue sufficiently distinct to be recognized by all the members of a population yet mild enough not to damage the trees. Finally, in tropical species-rich habitats, even if a population were magically to be synchronized in seed production at long intervals, it seems unlikely that the seed crop would be large enough to satiate the local seed predator community as one species only constitutes a relatively small fraction of the forest. Quite the opposite is the case if one of the common mid-latitude tree species is synchronized in fruiting. This subject is discussed further in Chapter 5.

3.4 Dispersal by wind

Wind-dispersed seeds appear to have evolved independently in practically every common tropical woody plant family (e.g., Bombacaceae, Sterculiaceae, Apocynaceae, Dipterocarpaceae, Leguminosae, Malpighiaceae, Bignoniaceae, Sapindaceae, Combretaceae, etc.). The convergence in fruit and seed shape is quite startling and a wide variety of fruit and seed parts contribute to the wings or buoyancy devices.

Even in tropical rainforests, wind-dispersed seeds are occasionally found on canopy-member trees, vines and epiphytes. They are absent from rainforest understory for the obvious reason that there is almost no wind there. In deciduous tropical forests, they are even found on understory shrubs. In a Costa Rican study by H. G. Baker, G. W. Frankie, and associates, of 105 tree species from a deciduous forest, 31 per cent were wind-dispersed (50 per cent had fleshy fruits, suggesting dispersal by animals). Several tropical canopy-member vine families have wind-dispersed seeds almost irrespective of their habitat (e.g., Apocynaceae, Asclepiadaceae, Bignoniaceae). Orchids, ferns and bromeliads very commonly have tiny wind-dispersed propagules even in the wettest forest. Wind-dispersed seeds are noticeably absent from woody plants at tropical elevations above about 2000 metres, but the reasons are not obvious.

Just as with temperate zone wind-dispersed species, the tropical ones have the disadvantage of producing a relatively dense seed fall quite close to the parent plant. Such dispersal is, however, conspicuously cheap per seed and is not dependent on the vagaries of animal hunger and density. It is unclear to what degree the loss of the potential accuracy and distance that can be achieved by other dispersal systems may be compensated for by large numbers of wind-dispersed seeds. Furthermore, in the forest environment, where the important considerations are the seedling's ability to survive defoliation and compete with other plants, large seeds are heavily selected for. This militates against dispersal by wind. Wind dispersal is most prominent in Southeast Asian Dipterocarpaceae forests, but in these forests it is satiation of local seed predators rather than dispersal far from the parent that appears to be the dominant escape strategy for forest tree seeds.

3.5 Dispersal by animals

Among woody plants in the tropics, seeds dispersed by clinging to fur are very rare. In contrast, seed dispersal by passage through the gut of a mammal or bird, or by being carried by a rodent, is the commonest form of seed dispersal in most tropical forest habitats. This is so from sea level to high elevations, from evergreen rainforest to desert. This is a curious form of dependence on vertebrates. If these animals were all removed from a tropical forest, many tree species would remain and the forest as a whole would persist. However, there would very likely be an immediate and rapid change in the proportional species composition of the forest, in the demographic properties of each tree population, and in the spatial relationship of the individuals of each species.

We have no detailed documentation of a naturally occurring seed shadow of even one tropical tree species with animal-dispersed seeds. However, the data at hand allows us to state with certainty that once documented, such seed shadows will have at least the following characteristics.

(a) They may take many forms, but in contemporary tropical communities, one is left with the impression that these seed shadows are more intense near the parent than far away. However, in a forest with a full complement of vertebrates and alternative food sources (a condition almost non-existent today), the array of dispersal agents may well remove *all* seeds from the vicinity of the parent. Such a thorough removal may be aided by pre-dispersal seed predation lowering the initial size of the seed crop.

(*b*) They will be much more attenuated than seed shadows of wind-dispersed species.

(*c*) They will contain major heterogeneities and these heterogeneities may change dramatically depending on the dispersal agents. For example, some species of Central American rodents may bury nearly all their seeds at the bases of particular large stumps or logs. Where the birds that eat *Cecropia* fruits are those of secondary succession, virtually all the seeds will be deposited in this type of vegetation, with the resulting seed shadow being linear along creek beds. A flying fox (bat) may deposit the large seeds of most of the mango fruits it eats in a pile below its feeding roost, and a neotropical frugivorous bat may defaecate many small seeds inside a hollow tree (at the base of its roost). A browsing ruminant may deposit many hundreds of seeds in one pile of faeces several miles from the parent plant.

(*d*) There may be strong intra-population heterogeneity of seed shadows. This is generated by the vagaries of which species of animals, in what numbers, happen to find a given tree's fruit crop, and what alternative fruit sources are in the vicinity of a reproducing tree. Dispersal agents can be satiated as well as can seed predators. Intra-population heterogeneity of animal-dispersed seed shadows should be much greater than that experienced with wind-dispersed species.

Given these heterogeneities, and given the obvious value of accurate dispersal, tropical fruits may be expected to show a number of traits that encourage certain dispersal agents and discourage others. Furthermore, animals may display traits that are adaptive in this context. A few are discussed below but this aspect of seed dispersal is almost totally unexplored for the tropics.

(*a*) Fruits dispersed by birds are generally brightly coloured, but those by bats are commonly green or yellow-green. As many animals that eat fruits either kill the seeds directly, or disperse them to the wrong place, advertising fruits to visually orienting diurnal dispersal agents may be costly. Needless to say, wind-dispersed seeds and fruits are the colour of dead plant tissue (brown), which may also be significant in hiding them from seed predators on the forest floor. In this context, we may note that in almost all cases, the *seeds* of animal-dispersed seeds are cryptically coloured.

(*b*) Fruits are usually oily or sugary (the mineral and protein content of wild tropical fruits is an unexplored area). In general, the oily fruits are associated with those species of vertebrates that gain much of their food from fruits; sugar content appears to be associated more with dispersal agents that are also insectivores or leaf-eaters. Fruits also contain a wide variety of secondary compounds which are responsible in part for their wide variety of flavours. In a particular habitat it is commonplace to have a number of species of fruits with quite similar flavours. The evolutionary convergence suggested by this is supported by the observation that these fruits are often all eaten by the same species of animals.

(c) Large size may prevent many seeds from being eaten by anything but a select few animals. However, large seeds are often carried in the feet by bats or in the mouth by terrestrial mammals. Small seeds (relative to the animal) not only pass through the gut easily, but they may be defaecated in clusters. There is no information on the adaptive value of seeds being deposited in various concentrations.

(d) There are various mechanisms that influence the rate of seed passage through animals. One that appears to be unique to the tropics is displayed by large neotropical birds (e.g., toucans, trogons) that eat large seeds and their accompanying thin fruit. After a short time in the bird gut, the soft seed is regurgitated intact after the gizzard has stripped off the fruit. In addition to being large, these seeds are apparently poisonous; presumably if digested they would be dangerous. A similar situation exists with those frugivorous ruminants that spit out the seeds when chewing their cud, thereby producing a very intense seed shadow at a few points in the habitat.

(e) The fruits in an individual crown tend to be matured either over a short time or a few per day for a very long time. In the former case, there is usually a large, multi-species, and generalized set of frugivores (ranging from pigs to monkeys to rats to birds) that feed on the fruit crop; as much as a tenth of the total crop may ripen in one day. Such crops are usually very conspicuous for their odour, colour and bustling animal community. Intra-population synchronization of such species is poorly documented; one can think of reasons why they might be either synchronized or widely spaced in time. In the case of those fruit crops with drawn-out ripening times (most common in smaller trees, vines and shrubs), new mature fruits may appear each day for as long as several months. The fruit crop is usually rather inconspicuous. Sometimes immature fruits as well as mature fruits of these species are brightly coloured (to serve as advertising), but in addition, it is likely that many such fruit crops are visited by birds or other vertebrates which know where the plant is and rely on getting a certain number of fruits from it each day. Such plant species also often display flowering of long duration, and the pollinators that visit them may be only rarely seen at mass-flowering species.

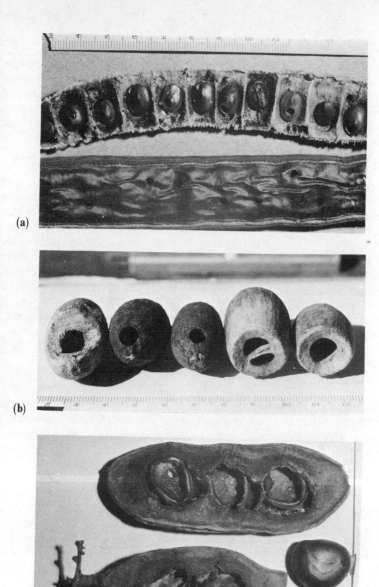

Plate 3 (a) On top, an opened seed pod of *Pithecellobium saman*, showing bruchid beetle exit holes in the seeds; at the bottom, the intact seed pod with bruchid exits through the pod wall (near Cañas, Guanacaste Prov., Costa Rica). (b) *Scheelea* palm nuts that have been chewed open by rodents (1st, 4th and 5th from the left), when the nuts were mature and fallen to the ground; the other nuts have bruchid exits (near Puntarenas, Costa Rica). (c) Pods of *Dioclea wilsoni* that were opened by a squirrel while the seeds were immature; mature seed on the right (near Vara Blanca, Heredia Prov., Costa Rica).

(*f*) There are very distinct seasonal patterns of fruiting (and flowering) at the community level in the tropics. What these patterns mean to the animals that eat the fruits, and to what degree the needs and heterogeneity of these animals produces the patterns (over evolutionary time) is as yet unclear. For example, it is certain that a fig tree that bears its fruit in the middle of the overall annual fruiting peak will be visited very differently than one that fruits out of phase.

There should be intense inter- and intra-specific competition for vertebrate dispersal agents. Fruit flavour, nutritional content, and timing should be the major traits of importance in this competition. These are all traits whose expression can be of considerable energetic and strategic cost to the plant. Simultaneously, we must note that the requirements of the animal community are not constant during the year nor between habitats. For example, fruits in general are much more in demand toward the end of the dry season, if only as a water source. Pregnant females may seek very different types of fruit than courting males since their nutritional demands are very different. In a year of poor rainy season plant growth, the biomass of dispersal agents may be much reduced during the following dry season.

3.6 Dispersal by other agents

As might be expected with a large number of species growing in the very great variety of habitats found in the tropics, there is a miscellany of very diverse dispersal types. Legumes commonly have explosive fruits, with torsion generated by the drying of the valves. A Costa Rican squash (Curcurbitaceae) fruit contains a device that throws the single seed like a bullet through the vegetation. A number of gourd-like hollow fruits float in rivers (Curcurbitaceae) and on the flatland floods generated by the first rains in deciduous forest (e.g., *Crescentia alata*, Bignoniaceae). In riparian vegetation of Costa Rican deciduous forest, there is a grass with small hooked hairs that stick to mammal fur. Mangrove fruits float on sea or estuary until they lodge on soil slightly newer than that occupied by their parents. A few rainforest seeds seem so large and heavy that one is tempted to label them as 'gravity dispersed' (e.g., the avocado *Persea*, Lauraceae). However, in forests with a normal animal complement, they are often moved away from the parent by large rodents. In tropical forests of very low plant species richness and reduced animal biomass, such as some dipterocarp forests of Borneo and Malaya, and *Ocotea* (Lauraceae) and *Eperua* (Leguminosae) forests of South America, there is almost no dispersal and most seedlings germinate directly below the parent.

4 Chemical Defences

4.1 Introduction

Animals are highly mobile predators and parasites of plants, and plants are sedentary prey and hosts. At best, the plant makes a single move when it is dispersed as a seed. In such a system, chemical defences are of paramount importance and it is not surprising to find them very well developed by plants. Following contemporary traditions the chemicals involved will be termed 'secondary compounds' since any given kind tends to be restricted to a small subset of the plant kingdom, and because any given kind is not generally involved in the cellular machinery common to most plants. 'Defensive compounds' would probably be a better name, except that many secondary compounds function in fruit flavours, flower perfumes, colouring, etc. Morphological defences such as thorns, corky bark and hard seed coats, and behavioural defences such as the timing of leaf growth, growth of callus tissue over wounds, and leaves sensitive to movement, are conspicuous in the tropics but have received almost no ecological study and so will receive little attention here. There is not even a single experimental field study documenting the impact of thorns on tropical browsing mammals.

We may expect defences to be best developed in the tropics, as the tropics does not have winter on its side, so to speak. However, within the tropics, we expect very great variation in this parameter. There are at least three clear causes of this variation.

4.1.1 Seasonality

The more severe the dry season, the more the dry season acts like a winter in reducing herbivore populations, and the more plants are able to escape from animals simply by doing such things as synchronizing leaf production with the 'lows' in herbivore density or activity. At the other end of the scale, the plants of rainforests have only their behaviour (e.g., timing of leaf flushes) and chemical traits to protect them. It is therefore not surprising to discover, for example, that livestock find far more palatable foliage among the wild plants of deciduous forest secondary vegetation than in rainforest.

4.1.2 Productivity

Independent of the variation generated by geographic heterogeneity of tropical climates, there should be another gradient from those places where the plant has a great deal of what is needed for growth (heat, water, and/or inorganic ions) to those habitats where such resources are in short supply. Though poorly understood for the tropics (because agricultural crops can hardly be grown there), the latter habitats are those such as deserts, forests above 2500 metres elevation, mangrove swamps, and vegetation on white sand soils. In the last three habitats, even when they have a very severe dry season, the foliage of perennials is usually evergreen and extremely rich in poisonous secondary compounds. While little explored, it can easily be argued that the high toxicity of the foliage in such places is the consequence of selection in a habitat where the loss of even small amounts of a leaf results in nutrient losses that are greater than the cost of substantial chemical defences. Furthermore, not only are trees in such areas evergreen, they often have leaves that live several years. Herbivore damage to such leaves may necessitate an earlier leaf replacement than if leaf replacement were based on shading alone.

4.1.3   Succession

Across both of the gradients mentioned above, plants of early successional stages have much less chemical defence than those of established forest or forest understory. This is because rapid growth is very important to young plants and those of the early stages of succession. This growth can be expected to take a larger part of the resource budget than is the case with a plant that has already established the position of most of its crown in the canopy, or that is waiting in the heavily shaded understory of the forest for a hole to open in the canopy above. This expectation is generally borne out by the relatively high density of herbivores in successional communities; the big herbivore population of tropical grasslands is perhaps the most conspicuous case but, in addition, the density of herbivorous insects is 5 to 10 times greater in secondary succession than in the shaded understory of rainforest.

4.2   Characteristics of secondary compounds

The secondary compounds that are found in tropical plants are extremely diverse chemically. For example, uncommon amino acids (amino acids not found in proteins) such as canavanine may mimic protein amino acids (canavanine differs from arginine only by having a CH_2 group replaced by an oxygen molecule). When accidentally incorporated in a protein, canavanine prevents its normal function. A large tropical vine seed such as *Dioclea* or *Canavalia* may contain as much as 10 per cent dry weight of this compound; when rat food contains slightly less than 1 per cent of the compound, rats will starve to death before eating it. Other uncommon amino acids that occur in high concentrations in tropical seeds, such as the 5 per cent dry weight L-DOPA found in *Mucuna* seeds, appear to detrimentally alter the concentrations of substrates in important physiological reactions in the animal that eats the seeds. Alkaloids are common constituents of tropical foliage. These nitrogen-rich compounds bind directly onto certain enzymes and prevent their proper physiological function. The alkaloids often act only on certain physiological systems and cause addiction, cessation of lactation, abortion or liver degeneration, and hence indirectly cause death of herbivores. Some saponins are leached from crushed tropical foliage or roots by native peoples as a fish poison. These compounds break down lipid-rich membranes of fish gills much as does soap. Cyanogenic glycosides are common in tropical plants; these compounds, like alkaloids and many other toxins, contain an active part (a cyanide molecule in this case) connected to a sugar molecule. When the plant tissue is crushed, its own enzymes and those of the herbivore split off the sugar, releasing the detrimental molecule. For example, a cyanogenic glycoside is being inactivated when the roots of manioc (=tapioca, *Manihot utilissima*, Euphorbiaceae) are crushed and soaked in water. Phenolic compounds (tannin and related organic acids), are commonly stored in vacuoles in older leaves and bark. When the vacuoles are broken by a herbivore, the released phenol binds very powerfully with any protein it encounters; the resulting compound is indigestible to most herbivores. The use of tannins found in mangrove bark for tanning leather is a commercial example. In addition to those general classes listed above, there is an immense miscellany of cardiac glycosides, latex, pyrethrins, carcinogens, and chemically undescribed toxic compounds to be found in tropical plants. A very large number of tropical tree families produce copious resins and gums when punctured by a herbivore (e.g., Euphorbiaceae, Guttiferae, Leguminosae, Sapotaceae, Meliaceae, Burseraceae, Dipterocarpaceae). In addition to literally 'gumming up' the feeding animal, these fluids often contain volatile toxic chemicals. Of a strictly physical nature, some tropical plants have large amounts of silicon crystals in their wood. These wear down the mandibles and teeth of herbivores (and of marine borers when their wood is used for pilings).

The major classes of secondary compounds are also found in temperate zone plants, but the number of kinds of each appears to be much greater in the tropics. However, the natural-products chemical

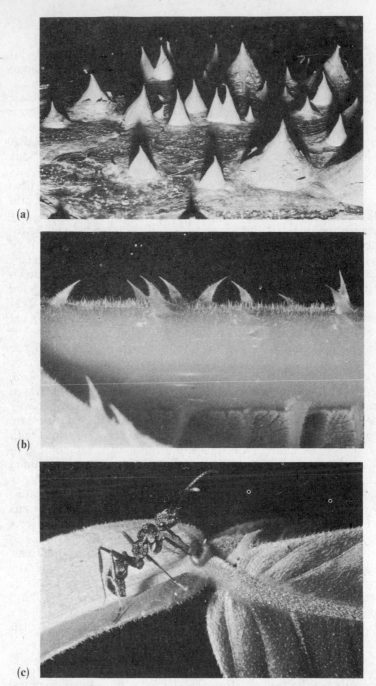

Plate 4 (a) Spines on a *Bombacopsis* tree trunk (the longest is about 1 inch long) which may deter large climbing mammals seeking the highly edible flowers (near Cañas, Guanacaste Prov., Costa Rica). (b) Urticating spines of *Urera baccifera* (Finca La Selva, Puerto Viejo, Heredia Prov., Costa Rica). (c) *Ectatomma* ant guarding an extra-floral nectary (and ready to prey on any small passing insect; same site as b).

literature has not been collated in such a manner as to permit documentation here. Unfortunately, most pharmacology of tropical secondary compounds has been with vertebrates and at the level of cell and tissue physiology. What happens when they are eaten by a wild herbivore, mixed with other compounds in the leaf and with other material eaten from another plant by the herbivore, and then processed by the microorganisms in the herbivore's gut, is an unexplored chemical wilderness and lies at the core of most animal-plant interactions.

4.3   Distribution of secondary compounds

The world is not coloured green to the herbivore's eyes, but rather is painted morphine, L-DOPA, calcium oxalate, cannabinol, caffeine, mustard oil, strychnine, rotenone, etc. Furthermore, these 'colours' are distributed among plant parts in a distinctly patterned manner. Phenolic compounds (including resins) are rarely found in seeds or in rapidly expanding tissues such as shoot tips and lateral cambium. Alkaloids seem to reach their highest concentrations in new leaves and shoot tips while tannins are most abundant in very old leaves. Resins are not found as defences in immature fruits, except in cases where the fruit wall is not destined to become the attractant tissue (e.g., in the pods of *Hymenaea courbaril*, where the fruit wall becomes a very hard defensive structure as the resin in the wall of the immature pod hardens). Toxic secondary compounds of all sorts are virtually absent from flower nectar, extra-floral nectar and pollen grains, for the obvious reason that it is generally adaptive for them to be eaten. In the case of pollen, it is curious that the pollen carried as a contaminant by animals other than bees is not toxic and hence does not avoid being scavenged by stingless bees (*Trigona*) and other insects. However, secondary compounds are found even in mature fruits. Such chemicals may be both defensive and adaptive in focusing the flow of seeds through certain members of the large potential array of dispersal agents in the habitat. Calcium oxalate crystals in the sweet flesh of bird-dispersed neotropical palm fruits may well serve this dual role. Defensive compounds in seeds are often nitrogen-rich alkaloids and uncommon amino acids, compounds that may also serve as nitrogen storage compounds for the rapidly growing seedling (though there is some evidence that the seedling may continue to use them as defensive compounds rather than metabolize them). Copious flow of resins, gums and latex is found primarily in woody structures. The secondary compound defences of roots are essentially unknown, but tropical tubers and other storage organs are well defended by such things as cortisone (a steroid in Dioscoreaceae tubers), cyanogenic glycosides (*Manihot*,

Euphorbiaceae), alkaloids (Convolvulaceae), and rotenone (Legu-minosae), etc.

Most plant parts have a number of different chemical defences. Some defences only function synergistically. One of the better known synerg-isms is that of nettles (Urticaceae), where the hollow spines on the plant inject histidine and acetylcholine; neither of these compounds by itself is painful, but the two together generate intense local pain. Cycasin, a carcinogenic compound found in cycads, only functions when the enzymes produced by bacteria in the gut of the herbivore split off the sugar molecule; germ-free rats are not affected by cycasin. A single plant may contain a dozen phenolic compounds or as many as 45 different kinds of alkaloids. However, the data for such a list may be based on plants of one 'species' collected at different sites and different stages, and this undoubtedly raises the number over that which can be found in one bite out of one plant.

In addition to direct toxicity of the secondary compounds, the nutri-tional background of the plant indirectly affects their toxicity. For example, tannins render protein indigestible but if a protein-rich food can be eaten with a tannin-rich food, the ill effects of the tannin may be overcome. A starved mammal is much more susceptible to poison-ing by uncommon amino acids in seeds than is a well fed one. It has recently been suggested that many tropical grasses are nutritionally much inferior to temperate zone grasses, owing to the former using C_4 photosynthesis. Secondary compounds, set against the background of a nutritionally inferior C_4 plant (which includes dicotyledons as well as grasses), may mean something very different to a herbivore than when in the high food value tissues of a C_3 plant.

Secondary compounds may also display distinctive patterns of dis-tribution within a tropical habitat. As mentioned previously, rapidly growing plants of early successional stages tend to be the most palat-able to herbivores, which suggests that they contain a lower concentra-tion of secondary compounds. As another example, there may be strong selection against one or both of any pair of plants growing in the same habitat and having similar chemical defences, since this makes them both available to one herbivore. Such a process should lead to strong intra-habitat diversity in secondary compounds as compared with inter-habitat diversity. The phenomenon should be most pro-minent within a given group of plant parts since, for example, animals that eat leaves are generally not the same as those that eat roots, and vice versa. For example, greater chemical diversity should be expected among different species of leaves than between the leaves and the roots that support them.

The example of white sand soils mentioned earlier is useful to emphasize how there may be substantial inter-habitat differences in overall amounts of secondary compounds. Around the tropics white sand soils commonly produce what are called 'blackwater' rivers. These rivers are very poor in nutrients and very rich in secondary compounds. These compounds are primarily phenolic (organic) acids (tannins); they are commonly called 'humic acids' and give the water its dark colour. The low nutrient content is probably partly responsible for the low productivity of blackwater rivers, but the high concentration of humic acids, which complex readily with proteins and mineral cations, is very likely to be responsible as well. We are then faced with the question of why does the rainwater passing through the vegetation that grows on white sand soil carry an exceptionally large amount of secondary compounds (tannins, etc.) into the river? Either this vegetation is exceptionally rich in secondary compounds, or the litter organisms are exceptionally incompetent at decomposing such compounds (which, after all, are present in all vegetation types), or both. The former explanation appears to be true both through chemical observation of the foliage itself, and through an examination of the plant families that constitute most of the biomass in the vegetation (e.g., Guttiferae, Dipterocarpaceae, Leguminosae, Anacardiaceae, Burseraceae, Apocynaceae, Euphorbiaceae, Theaceae, Magnoliaceae, Casuarinaceae, Podocarpaceae, Ericaceae). The latter explanation appears to be true in that when the long-lived and leathery leaves arrive on the ground, it appears necessary for them to leach for many months before they are sufficiently free of secondary compounds for micro-organisms to decompose them further. On some white sand soils this results in a metre or so of litter below the trees and even deep peat accumulations in the same manner as in temperate zone peat bogs (which also produce blackwater rivers). Such vegetation based on white sand has an extremely reduced standing crop of animals. The low animal biomass is undoubtedly due in part to the very low primary productivity of the forest. However, the forest is also putting much of what it does produce into tissue that is nearly unharvestable by animals, since a leaf with a high tannin content is inedible to most herbivores.

4.4 Defences against secondary compounds

So far nothing has been said of how the animals counter the chemical defences of tropical plants. Unfortunately next to nothing is known of how tropical animals do it, so we are forced to infer from temperate zone examples. There is, however, no reason to suspect that tropical animals detoxify tannin, canavanine or morphine, for example, in a manner different from temperate zone animals. It should be emphasized that many tropical herbivores appear to be specialists on amazingly toxic plants. The larvae of the bruchid beetle *Caryedes brasiliensis* normally mature on a pure diet of *Dioclea* seed content which, as was mentioned earlier, contains up to 10 per cent dry weight of the toxic amino acid canavanine. The carcinogen (cycasin) found in cycad leaves and seeds passes through the gut wall of a specific arctiid moth caterpillar that feeds on the plant, is re-combined with a sugar molecule, and sequestered just under the cuticle. When the caterpillar moults, the compound is shed with the old cuticle. There is at least one species of moth larva that can eat the alkaloid-rich seeds of *Erythrina* (Leguminosae).

There appear to be two major ways of dealing with highly toxic compounds in tropical (and temperate) foliage. One way is to be small relative to the food source, and specialize on one kind of food and one kind of detoxification (as mentioned above). For example, of 111 species of bruchid beetles collected to date breeding in the seeds of Costa Rican deciduous forest tree seeds, each of 102 of them seems to have only one host plant and each is different from that of the others. While this is a rather extreme case, it is probably much more representative than is generally appreciated. Interestingly, if many of these bruchids are examined over their entire geographic range (e.g., Mexico to Panama), it will be found that each species has a number of plant hosts; they are, however, locally quite species-specific, implying that local populations excel at detoxifying one kind of defensive compound only.

The other major detoxification system involves animals that are large with respect to the host and eat a small amount of many species of plants. Many mammals are in this category, with certain ruminants probably being the most adept. A ruminant may be viewed as a complex compost heap, with much of the animal's feeding behaviour and physiology designed to maintain a healthy and diverse microbial community whose major task is the detoxification of the wide variety of secondary compounds fed to it. It is probable, for example, that by feeding on one plant species, a mammal could select for a bacterial gut flora that is very efficient at detoxifying the essential oils found in the foliage of one species of tropical tree; however, when that tree lost its leaves or was defoliated by the herbivore, the animal would have severe problems in switching to a new species of food plant. It is not surprising, therefore, to find that many tropical ruminants eat small amounts of a very large number of species of plants. An interesting exception is an animal such as the proboscis monkey of Malaysian mangrove swamps. This animal subsists almost entirely on a diet of extremely tannin-rich mangrove foliage. In a certain sense it is acting like a large insect. It can do this because mangroves exist in large evergreen stands and all the species appear to have high concentrations of tannins as their defences.

4.5 Cost of secondary compounds

Perhaps the two most difficult aspects of the chemical ecology of animal-plant interactions are (1) knowing what the compounds cost the plant (that is, how much would its fitness be raised if it did not make and sequester the compounds), and (2) what would happen to the plant were the plant deprived of all or part of them? Careful quantitative biochemical economics may get at the first question but the second is probably unapproachable with most wild plants owing to the difficulty of experimentally removing their chemicals. However, ant-plants offer an approach by analogy.

Ant-plants are found through the tropics. In most cases, the ants live in hollow stems or thorns and are provided with all their food by the plant. This may be direct, as in the neotropical acacias (*Acacia* spp., Leguminosae) where the ants eat extra-floral nectar and protein- and lipid-rich food bodies produced by the leaves, or indirect, as in the case of the African *Barteria* (Passifloraceae). In this tree, the ants raise scale insects on the inside of the hollow stems and harvest nectar and offspring from the scale insects as food. In return, the ants in ant-plants generally protect the plant from herbivores and vines by fiercely attacking any foreign object that touches the plant. In effect, the ants are analogous to a general purpose chemical defence. Their cost to the plant is fairly obvious. The magnificent thing about them is that they can be removed without damaging the plant. When the ants are removed from Central American swollen-thorn acacias, for example, the small tree lives an average of 3 to 12 months, depending on the habitat-specific attack rate of the herbivores. The tree virtually never reaches reproductive maturity unless occupied by an ant colony. The death of the tree is directly due to intense herbivory by many species of insects, insects that normally are deterred by the ants and feed on other plants in the habitat (and on juvenile acacias that do not yet have ant colonies). Furthermore, in some habitats, shading by vines that use the unoccupied acacia for a trellis is an indirect cause of death. With the example of the acacia, it is possible to demonstrate the validity of comparing the ants with chemical defences. It has now been shown that the ant-acacia lacks the chemical defences (e.g., cyanogenic glycosides) common among non-ant-acacias. It is most likely that as the ant-acacia interaction evolved the chemical defences were selected against, since they were a cost that did not repay itself in lowered herbivory. The analogy is even exact to the level that there are some herbivorous insects that have evolved behavioural mechanisms for avoiding the ants, just as all other plants have some herbivores that have breached their chemical defences.

4.6 Evolutionary considerations

Defences and herbivores have been discussed as though the plant dealt with them as distinct from other challenges in the environment. However, this is clearly not the case, and especially so in a tropical environment where there may be many challenges of approximately equal severity. When parts of a leaf are repeatedly removed, the plant perceives the event as a reduction in photosynthetic yield by its leaves; it may well be indifferent to the cause of damage, whether it be by a browsing mammal, a butterfly larva, a falling branch or fungal attack. Likewise, an evolutionary response to this tiny reduction in fitness may occur anywhere in the plant's genome. For example, if the damage were due to a butterfly larva, the evolutionary response of the plant may be the appearance of a new secondary compound that eliminates a root-feeding beetle larva. If the damage were by a mammal, the response might be the evolution of spines, or on the other hand, the evolution of a leaf placement that reduced leaf damage by falling debris. Of course, there may also be no evolutionary response, with the result that the plant just becomes a little bit rarer. In short, if a plant's fitness is lowered by a new challenge in the environment, the reduction may be partly alleviated by internal adjustments that cost less than the reduction. Of course, each new challenge must result in some tiny overall lowering of fitness for the plant. This can be expressed by such events as change in habitat 'preference', relative abundance in the habitat, or persistence over contemporary or evolutionary time.

5 Community Structure

5.1 Introduction

It should be evident from the previous chapters that the tropics contain extremely diverse habitats, even more so than do the mid-latitudes. This chapter discusses briefly some of the patterns that are evident if tropical habitats are classified by so-called community traits, such as the number of species of plants, their spatial distributions, and the number of individuals in each species.

5.2 Species-poor vegetation

While the tropics are famous for species-rich forests, a very large variety and acreage of tropical habitats are not extraordinarily rich in species of plants. For example, it is commonplace for a given successional sere in a mangrove swamp to contain only 1 or 2 species of mangroves. Even the most extensive mangrove swamps, those of Southeast Asia, contain only 5 to 25 species of trees. Even within the mangrove habitat there are, however, latitudinal gradients in species richness; the mangrove swamps of the subtropics have only 1 to 4 tree species. Tropical deserts commonly contain as few as 3 to 20 species of large woody plants in a particular habitat, and often lack the huge flora of ephemeral herbs found in temperate zone deserts. At elevations above 2500 metres in the tropics, and sometimes as low as 1500 metres, it is commonplace to encounter forests with most of the trees belonging to 2 or 5 species. Tropical freshwater swamps and marshes are characterized by many square kilometres covered largely by one species of tree (e.g., *Shorea alba* (Dipterocarpaceae) peat swamp forest in Sarawak) or herb (e.g., papyrus marshes of Uganda) with scattered individuals of a few other species mixed in. On very poor soils, such as the white sands mentioned in Chapter 4, a given exposure and drainage type is commonly occupied by a very small number of woody species. For example, *Eperua* spp. (Leguminosae) constitutes well over 70 per cent of the large trees in a number of white sand habitats of lowland Brazil and Guyana. The understory of shrubs and small trees in *Eperua* forest is likewise species-poor. The great grasslands of Africa display a species richness not substantially different from temperate zone prairies; neotropical savannahs are particularly species-poor. Island vegetation, even in the tropics, commonly may contain very few species.

Massive defoliations by insects do occur in such species-poor vegetation, but only rarely. These vegetation types are not noticeably unstable and deny the contemporary dogma that highly diverse vegetation is mandatory in the tropics for stability of the interaction between herbivores and their food. Such vegetation types are, however, characterized by either low primary productivity (e.g., high elevation sites), low harvestable productivity (e.g., secondary compound-rich vegetation on white sand soils), and/or subject to an extremely efficient and inescapable consumer (e.g., fire in African grasslands).

5.3   Species-rich vegetation

With the exception of the tropical grasslands mentioned above, where the huge animal biomass is really just the outcome of a fire-adapted vegetation, the tropical vegetation types poor in plant species are also very poor in animal biomass and/or species. The habitats rich in species of plants are also comparatively rich in species of animals (and commonly, overall biomass of animals). Furthermore, the environment is generally one where the animals can be active all year round if their host plant is available. This means that the plant has only its behaviour, its defensive chemistry, and its intra-population spacing for escape. Neither of the first two defences would appear to be adequate for absolute escape by any species of plant, since herbivores (and especially insects and micro-organisms) have many generations per woody plant generation (and therefore are likely to produce resistance to strains faster than the plant evolves defences). Attention should therefore be focussed on intra-population spacing and its relationship to herbivory in order to understand how to pack a large number of species of plants into a habitat.

Species-rich tropical forests not only have many plant species, but each tree species constitutes only a small fraction of the forest biomass represented by its particular life form. Furthermore, the adults are far more widely scattered than would be the case were they to mature in proportion to the number of seeds that arrive at any particular distance from the parent tree. We do not yet have a well-verified hypothesis as to why this is so, but we do have a rough start. In short, the best circumstantial evidence suggests that the animals are keeping any one species of plant from becoming common enough to competitively oust the others of its life form. The herbivores are producing great intra-population distances, rather than such distances being an evolved trait *per se*. It could well be that the problem in understanding why there are so many tree species in some tropical habitats is one of what ecological forces produce the greatest distances between conspecifics, thereby allowing the largest possible number of species in the habitat. It seems likely that the problem has very little to do with the *rate* of speciation or extinction in the tropics. It is obvious that each species-rich tropical habitat (and even more important, each species-poor habitat) is constantly being bombarded by seeds of far more species than it contains—the problem then becomes what determines the per cent of incoming species that survive?

The process can be visualized as operating more or less in the following manner. Each time an individual tree produces a seed crop, it has in effect produced a minor and local population explosion for that species. If there is another conspecific adult doing the same, close by in either time or space, they may mutually infect each other with host-specific pre-dispersal seed predators. In fact, the closer the adult trees, the greater will be the reduction in seed crop before dispersal (thereby lowering the probability that *any* new adults will result from that season's seed crop). Once the seeds are dispersed, a second process can be expected. Those seeds that end up close to the parent tree should be subject to much higher seed predation and seedling herbivory than those that are dispersed far away (unless, of course, they have the misfortune of landing near another reproducing conspecific). This is because the animals have both the high concentration of juveniles and the parent tree to use as a flag to locate prey and hosts. In effect, the animals create a zone around the parent tree where no matter how good a competitor it is, it is unlikely to produce another adult. The outcome is that this space is then relatively more available for the adults of other tree species. For obvious reasons, the more host-specific the animals in such a system, the more effective they will be at lowering the density of their hosts and keeping them widely spaced.

In short, the more effective the animals are at moving between seed crops in space *and* time and at eliminating juveniles that are close together, the more tree species should be expected in the community. In other words, the more inimical to the animals the period between the times of production of plant juveniles, and the longer the plants can wait between seed crops (yet be synchronized in their production), the less likely the animals will be to prevent the best plant competitors from taking over a habitat characterized by a particular soil, weather, slope, etc. Also, herbivores specializing on the new foliage of adult trees should have an effect much the same as do the predators on the juveniles. Viewed in this light, it is not surprising to find that habitates poor in herbivores are poor in tree species. However, the direct demonstration of the implied causal relationship still requires extensive experimental documentation.

Unfortunately, there is very little information of what would happen to a species-rich tropical forest if the seed- and seedling-eating animals, or the leaf-eaters, were removed. Where the mammals and birds have been removed (e.g., in most heavily hunted African forests), there appear to be no records being kept of changes. In some open forest-savannah habitats, such as African game parks, the opposite experiment has obvious results. The increase in mammals well over sustained yield carrying capacity has resulted in dramatic changes in plant species composition and community structure. However, tropical islands offer an interesting clue to the long term effects of removal of the animals. Many lack a substantial herbivore community, even when undisturbed. Associated with this, the plants there tend to form dense monospecific patches and thickets. These are often the same or similar to species found widely scattered at low densities on the mainland in habitats or very similar physical conditions to those on the islands. It is hard to escape the conclusion that if the appropriate seed- or seedling-eating and/or leaf-eating animals were introduced, they would greatly thin out these pure stands and leave room for species from other habitats and even from the mainland. Where large herbivores have been introduced on islands, they are generally ruminants such as goats. They can feed on a very large number of species of plants and instead of reducing the density of one species, so that others can grow there, they tend to reduce all. However, with time this should also lead to an increase in species richness, as species evolve resistance to the goats and resistant species succeed in establishment owing to their favoured anti-herbivore status.

5.4 Succession

So far this discussion has been concerned with habitats that are large enough to contain all the successional seres or stages normally associated with that habitat, or with a single successional sere. However, distinct differences in community structure are evident between the various successional stages to be found in a tropical habitat. Before listing some of the ways that tropical succession differs from temperate, it must be emphasized that there is tremendous inter-habitat variation in these parameters in the tropics. The differences between succession on a tropical rainforest, in a monospecific stand of oak on a tropical mountain top, and in a mangrove swamp are immense and undocumented in a systematic manner.

For an example, let us contrast succession in a lowland species-rich tropical rainforest on average soils with that in a mid-latitude mixed hardwood forest. When a large tree falls in the tropical forest, the following statements can be made:

(1) The species that first appear there are generally different from the

set that grows at the sites of other tree falls, whereas in the mid-latitude forest, a similar combination of species appears at all sites.

(2) The species of tree that finally fills the gap is very unlikely to be the same as the one that vacated it, whereas in the mid-latitude forest it is likely to be the same.

(3) As succession proceeds, we may recognize many more 'stages' than in the mid-latitude forest, if stages are defined by the change from one array of life forms to another, or from one species complex to another.

(4) If a number of equal-aged and middle-aged successional seres are compared, it will be found that there will be many species that are found in only a few of them, while in the mid-latitude forest, most species of a sere will be found in all replicates.

(5) The time to produce an adult canopy-member tree will depend greatly on the initial species in the tropical disturbed site, while this does not appear to be so much the case in mid-latitude forest.

(6) It is much more difficult to determine when 'succession' has 'ended' than in a mid-latitude forest.

In addition to these differences, there is another set of differences associated with different kinds of initial disturbance, such as flooding, river bank erosion, fires, and hurricane damage. Each of these types can occur in the same habitat and seems to lead to a relatively unique assemblage of plant species and proportions, more so than appears to be the case in mid-latitude forest. However, these are only the writer's field impressions. There are no quantitative studies that would allow a more definitive statement. The same, of course, applies to the list of six points in the previous paragraph.

The final and huge complication to be mentioned here is that disturbance by contemporary man has now badly blurred the distinctions that were once possible in tropical secondary succession. Not only does he selectively remove and encourage certain plant and animal species, but he repeatedly and capriciously deflects succession at various ages and with various degrees of completion. When the initial stock of plants is rich in species and life forms, one outcome of such habitat treatment is the production of plant assemblages that are not found in any natural successional sere. For example, there is no natural habitat that even approximates the species composition and proportions of a tropical abandoned corn field, road shoulder, or overgrazed pasture.

There is a particularly difficult problem with comparison of tropical vegetation, be they small plots (all of which must represent some stage in 'succession') or areas large enough to contain most of the successional 'stages'. We have virtually no understanding of the population structure of each tree species, nor what population structure may be regarded as representative of a species in an area under a given disturbance regime. In fact, in a species-rich forest, it may well turn out to be a meaningless abstraction to speak of a 'climax forest', except when we compare many square kilometres of the forest with an adjacent cleared area.

Throughout this discussion it is of utmost importance that the reader bear in mind that the vegetation regenerating in tropical fields and pastures, the contemporary vegetation of much of the lowland tropics, is drawn from a wide variety of habitats. Much of the behaviour, chemistry and morphology of the individual plants is no longer adaptive in the context under which it evolved. For example, it should not be surprising to find species flowering at clearly maladaptive times or having a life form that is suicidal (e.g., a shrub in a field of vines). Many of the 'populations' in such fields may be non-reproductive and maintained by seed flow in space and time from other types of succession or successional seres where the plant can reproduce.

It is commonplace to compare the tropical open field with the canopy of mature forest. Usually this is done because the weather conditions appear superficially similar in the two microhabitats. However, it is instructive in the context of this chapter to point out some of the ways that this is a misleading comparison from the viewpoint of the herbivorous animals that live in the field and adjacent 'climax' rainforest.

(1)   Almost none of the species of plants are the same in the two habitats; it is rare to find even a seedling of an undisturbed forest canopy-member tree in the very early stages of succession.

(2)   The proportions of life forms are very different in each of the two habitats; for example, large epiphytes are almost entirely absent from the early stages of succession, while continuously flowering and growing plants (as are many herbs) are largely absent from the forest canopy.

(3)   The plant species composition of early succession changes rapidly within a hectare or two, while an area of equal size in the forest canopy has a very slow turnover rate of species.

(4)   The scale is very different in the two sites. An insect moving 50 metres in a field will encounter many species of plants and most of the species in that habitat; one moving 50 metres in the forest canopy may encounter only a very few species of trees and only a tiny fraction of the total in the habitat. In short, from the viewpoint of a sedentary animal, the forest canopy may be much less diverse than a field.

6 Tropical Agriculture

6.1 Introduction

In the narrow sense, agriculture is applied plant and animal ecology. In the broad sense it is an integral part of an agroecosystem not only involving agriculture but also moulded by sociology, economics, politics, history and other human cultural traits. More in the tropics than in any other part of the world, agriculture must be regarded as part of an agroecosystem rather than as a system unto itself if productivity is to even approximate a sustained yield of human desiderata.

The contemporary tropical agroecosystem may be characterized by the following traits:

(1) Its goals are generally unsatisfactory compromises arising from the conflict of a local culture that wants food and power (=money) for its use, and a foreign culture that wants food and raw materials and is interested in paying only what it has to pay, rather than what is the resource drain on the country that is exporting the goods.

(2) As its model for a standard of living, the tropical country commonly uses one of the many mid-latitude countries that are based on much greater agricultural resources than the tropical one can marshal.

(3) Per hectare or so of tillable land, tropical soils and pests are generally much worse than are temperate ones, largely due to the lack of a cold winter.

In this short chapter, at best it is only possible to expand superficially on these and other peripheral aspects of tropical agroecosystems. Even a superficial approach is, however, better than an omission, since that would constitute tacit approval of the contemporary agricultural mismanagement of most of the tropics. This is a huge area, one deserving of an as yet unwritten large book. Only a few things that seem especially important have been chosen, starting with the more classical biological aspects, and finishing with the more socio-economic ones. Tropical agriculture is stressed in this book because for far too long it has been convenient for mid-latitude cultures and contemporary tropical planners to pretend that what was wrong with tropical agriculture was simply blind application of mid-latitude agricultural policy.

6.2   Continuous warmth

The tropical farmer does not have winter on his side. While continuous warmth might appear of value in growing crops, it brings with it a large number of very severe problems.

(1)   If water is available long enough for continuous cropping, then pests and weeds simply build up in the fields. A mid-latitude farmer makes good use of the depression in the number of pests that occur in winter. It is no accident that the lowland tropical areas with greatest farming production are located in areas that once bore deciduous forest yet have an intense and reliable rainy season.

(2)   If crop rotation is used as a method of breaking pest population increases, then it must be done in such a manner that the other crops used by the pest are very far away in space. This, of course, was one of the original selective pressures for the evolution of so-called 'primitive' shifting agriculture. In a certain sense, several miles of forest between one field and the next one may be equivalent to a northern winter.

(3)   Even in areas with a severe dry season, tropical pest populations are often not severely depressed by the weather but rather by the removal of the crop. This means that if alternate crops or wild hosts are available (such as are found in irrigated fields or shady riparian vegetation), the pests may also be available whenever the crop is planted.

(4)   If a field is left unused as a way of breaking the pest cycle, weeds will continue to grow in it. It is generally necessary to allow the regeneration in fallow fields to progress to where the seed reservoir in the soil has died and the weedy species are no longer present to sprout from roots when the vegetation is cut and/or burned. The same concept applies to the removal of animal pests by fallow systems.

(5)   The continuously warm soil leads to a very rapid decomposition of organic matter whenever there is rainfall or soil water. Coupled with intense tropical rains during the growing season, this means that there is almost no reservoir of minerals, as they are rapidly leached from the soil when released from the organic litter. This phenomenon makes the application of chemical fertilizers very difficult since they disappear so rapidly, and since they must be applied in carefully measured proportions to avoid damaging roots when the added fertilizer is the only nutrient available. It means that tree crops (which begin to approximate the closed nutrient loop represented by intact forest) are at an advantage but these have those well known disadvantages that any long-term investment in tree crops is satisfactory only in a society accustomed to long-term but small yield.

(6)   Once a crop is harvested, the continually warm weather means

that it is continually susceptible to stored-product pests and microbial decomposition. This aspect is further complicated by the problem that many tropical foodstuffs lack well-developed physiological dormancy mechanisms.

6.3 Plant defences

When a mid-latitude farmer produces a monoculture, the close juxtaposition of conspecific plants is not a gross departure from natural circumstances, and we do not expect herbivores to be given a severe edge by this act. The tropical monoculture field is, however, a great departure from natural plant spacing in most areas of high primary productivity. In tropical monocultures, insects that are behaviourally and morpho-logically equipped to move long distances in searching out widely spaced hosts are suddenly confronted with a huge and easily located food supply. This places a premium on the farmer being able to keep his fields of conspecifics widely spaced. It also places a premium on secondary compounds as a major line of defence.

Secondary compounds are, however, a great problem in tropical foodstuff agriculture. (Rubber, chocolate, coffee, tea, and spices are secondary compounds in themselves and thus not included here.) The majority of human food plants are bred from wild ancestors that were chemically unprotected (grains, nuts and fruits), or else have had these compounds bred out of them to increase their palatability. Vegetables are a good example. Such plants or plant parts are then especially susceptible to pests when grown in pure stands, but yet in the tropics there is no way to grow the pure stands at a time of year when pests are particularly sparse. Even when planted in highly mixed stands, only certain carefully chosen mixtures are effective at reducing pest popula-tions. This is partly due to the close proximity of conspecifics even if scattered in a field, but more likely due to many different species of crop plants being edible to a single pest owing to their similar (bland) chemical content. In an environment where a very large part of herbivore host-specificity is based on plant chemistry, the loss of defensive com-pounds also makes the crop plant available to a relatively much larger number of insects than is the case at mid-latitudes. Lettuce is perhaps the most extreme case; almost any animal will eat it.

The classical answer to the absence of natural plant defences is to put the secondary compound back on the outside of the plant in the form of synthetic chemical pesticides. Apart from the problem that this raises the cost of a crop whose value is likely to be marginal already, resistance must be expected among tropical insects just as among those of mid-latitudes. Resistance is developed more rapidly among tropical insects because they have more generations per year than in higher latitudes, and because tropical herbivore genomes are probably more experienced at evolving mechanisms of detoxifying chemical defences than are those of mid-latitudes. Breeding resistance back into a crop plant, in order to keep ahead of the insect pest, is at best a viable proposition where the generation time of the insect is roughly equal to that of the plant. This makes tree crops again a bad bet, unless they are being grown for non-foodstuffs and happen to have pests that do not increase when the trees are put close together in a plantation.

Biological control programmes in the topics are commonly proposed as high value solutions to the pest problem. However, this suggestion is based on the often doubtful assumption that tropical herbivores are kept in check in the first place by predators and parasites. The majority of successful tropical biological control programmes have been on islands, where fauna and flora are reduced and much more like mid-latitude communities. Furthermore, they have been in agroecosystems that had available to them the knowledge, long-term stability, and cultural machinery to make them work. Scientists are confronted with the real problem in tropical agriculture that it is not even known if elimination of most of the predators and parasites together with some of the herbivores, by massive habitat destruction or pesticide use, would produce higher or lower yields.

6.4 Socio-economic problems

We could go on at some length about the individual biological problems, but the reader can probably walk a few miles in the tropical countryside and see most of them for himself. The mid-latitude reader need only use his imagination in asking what would happen to his own agricultural system were the three points in Section 6.1 true of it. The point to be stressed here is that for each area of the tropics, local peoples in the past have co-evolved agroecosystems that take into account the local biology and produce a relatively sustained yield for a relatively small number of self-supporting people. Such agroecosystems were almost invariably characterized by such things as (a) tight control over individual action by a village council and tradition, (b) much of the crop being rotated from area to area at 1 to 5 year intervals, (c) most of the village land being left fallow and used for wild crops and protein, (d) highly diverse crops carefully interdispersed in time and space, (e) very specific and adaptive horticultural practices evolved for each crop, (f) farming activities carefully integrated such that the labour needs for the different crops and other activities were compatible, (g) leisure time planned into the agroecosystem as a desirable product, etc.

It is obvious that, if carefully done, such systems can be expanded to include more than a local village, make use of economies of scale, and even produce some surplus for use outside the region. However, the forces shaping contemporary change in tropical agriculture have not been nearly so moderate.

Perhaps one of the largest problems is to confuse the carefully controlled and well integrated shifting cultivation (slash and burn agriculture) of relatively undisturbed tropical cultures with present-day practices. Today 'slash and burn' agriculture commonly involves little more than cutting down the forest, growing a crop, and moving on to uncut forest. There is no plan of fallow or return, and the abandoned fields are turned to brushy pastures. This type of agriculture is little more than a cheap mechanism to clear the forest and to temporarily deal with human populations that are increasing rapidly because they have been freed of the strictures of village traditions and disease. Such activity has given the original slash and burn agriculture an undeserved bad name.

Associated with this type of land use is the problem that many tropical governments or large land holders have in various ways ensured the use of the best soils for agricultural or other natural products that bring cash revenues to the owners and produce food crops for large cities. Forced onto the poorer types of soil, the tropical peasant farmer has even more difficulty in trying to develop a sustained yield agriculture. As the large land owners measure their profits on a short-term scale and in cash that is generally not returned to the local agroecosystem, the system progresses toward a system of soil mining rather than sustained yields. Ironically, it is the large land holdings that should be on poor soil, and the intensive small scale agriculture on the good soil, if anywhere.

This system can be described by the simple statement that it is a system without direct feedback loops. Currently, if the rainforest farmer destroys his land, he simply moves on or moves to the city. If the banana crop of a large land owner eventually fails, he simply cuts down more rainforest or consolidates his losses and invests in some entirely different industry. It is obvious that politicians and nations have been fighting over this problem and its consequences for many years, and there seems to be no palatable solution; the unpalatable ones are obvious. There are, however, a few glaring holes in tropical agroecosystems as they now stand:

(1)   The borders of most tropical countries were established by mid-latitude countries dividing up a resource pie, rather than having their borders based on the amounts of resources needed to support contemporary major education, health, government, etc. systems.

(2)   With the value of exports set by the purchasing country rather

than by the actual cost of producing them as based on some world-wide set of values, it is impossible for a tropical country to plan around a sustained income, or even evaluate the real carrying capacity of its lands (a far cry from the local village system).

(3) Most tropical countries get their aspirations for a standard of living by watching the mid-latitude countries, without taking stock of the fact that this high standard of living is based on mid-latitude high agricultural productivity, and on resources obtained from tropical countries at value far below cost.

(4) As the agricultural money in tropical countries is concerned almost entirely with export materials, that is where the research is. Local foodstuffs are a trivial item in high quality research in tropical agriculture.

(5) When solutions are proposed for tropical agricultural systems they are almost invariably highly reductionist. For example, when biological control is called cheap, it is because we do not charge to it the cost of an educational system that will produce farmers sufficiently educated to deal with its complexity in the absence of guiding professionals. Or, when rice is given as an example of a high yield tropical monoculture crop, what is left out is that modern tropical peoples are generally no more interested in spending hours hand-transplanting rice seedlings than are their mid-latitude counterparts.

We do not need more food in the tropics. We require effective mechanisms for determining the carrying capacity for people of a given distribution of standard of living, and for encouraging people to live at that density. To this end, there is no necessity for more birth control technology; virtually all peoples of the world have, and have had, birth control methods at their disposal. It would be better to have sociological pressures that make people *not want* to produce large families. Further reductionist research on how to increase the yield of this bean or that rice strain at the expense of the plant's drought tolerance or pest resistance is no longer essential. What is wanted is a system to integrate and consolidate what is already known in the tropical scientific and folklore community at large, and get it operating in the context of sustained-yield agroecosystems. We need a system that will show people that the tropics are a finite resource base just like the rest of the world.

7 Suggested Field Studies

7.1 Introduction

It is important to realize that one's preferences in tropical research projects depend on one's goals as well as one's expertise. Here, nine research programmes are suggested that may generate ideas and information of use to a wide number of different philosophies. It should be evident that we can never hope to approach even a description of tropical biology in its full complexity; at best we can aim for understanding. As mentioned in the first chapter, much of what we need to know of the tropics can be collected with little more than a notebook and ruler. The critical resource is time on the site and imagination in planning and analysis of the data gathered. Most of the experiments suggested here require a brief bit of intense effort in establishment and final recording of results, with a long wait in between. Such a time lag is no problem to the tropical resident.

Ironically, once much of the research suggested here has been carried out, the worker will often discover that the comparable study has never been done in the extra-tropical regions, or has been done so poorly as to be of no use in comparison. In designing the studies suggested below, it is imperative that the data be gathered so as to test at least certain simple hypotheses, and yet simultaneously be adventurous in approach and analysis so as to maximize the probablity of generating new ideas. Of all areas of the world, tropical biology does not need new cakes baked with old recipes, but rather some new recipes.

Before going into detail, one comment applies to all of the suggested studies. As with most scientific investigations, they are of no use whatsoever if the findings are not made available to other scientists and published in journals regularly available in libraries throughout the world. Annual reports, mimeographed handouts, unpublished theses, and talks at conferences might as well have never been done if the material contained is not also published. Refereed journals are obviously better for the author and the reader. While journals rich in tropical studies are clearly appropriate, prospective authors should realize that their papers will also receive very interested attention in the journals devoted heavily to the biology of mid-latitude plants.

7.2   Leaf life span

Knowledge of the life spans of tropical leaves is essential for under-standing the economics and evolution of deciduous behaviour, leaf internal morphology, leaf chemistry, litter dynamics, fruiting patterns, etc. The mechanics of the research are simple. The petioles of new individual leaves can be ringed by light-weight bird bands (rings) or the individual leaves mapped on their branches. Since it is ridiculous to think of doing this for all plants in a tropical habitat, the leaves should be chosen so that the data tests hypotheses such as:

(a)   leaves on the lower sides of evergreen crowns have a longer life than do leaves on the upper sides of the same crowns;

(b)   leaves of evergreen rainforest adult trees are replaced more often than are the leaves of their saplings below;

(c)   leaves damaged by herbivores are replaced more rapidly than intact leaves;

(d)   leaf life is proportional to degree of chemical and morphological protection;

(e)   leaf life is proportional to tree age, health, reproductive state, nutrition, etc.

7.3   Response to defoliation

To understand why a plant behaves as it does, it is essential to know how it reacts when under stress. Defoliation is easily quantified and easy to position carefully in time with respect to such discrete events as fruiting, flowering, beginning of the rainy season, age of the leaf, age of the plant, etc. Defoliation experiments require little more than a pair of clippers (secateurs) and a map of the plant. Gross defoliation may even be achieved chemically, especially if done with a chemical that attacks only the leaves (such as paraquat). Care must be taken to ensure that what is removed is the only part damaged. For example, if the intent is to simulate beetle shot-hole feeding damage of 25 per cent, then holes should be punched out of 25 per cent of the leaf surface rather than removing 25 per cent of the leaves. Defoliation experiments should be designed to mimic the effects of challenges normally encountered by the plant. The effects should be recorded over long and short periods. Long-term records are important since a plant has many options for internal reaction to damage, such as reducing future seed crops, reduc-ing wood or leaf production and slowing crown expansion. A par-ticularly interesting procedure is to ask defoliation questions of different parts of the same crown, and thereby determine to what degree a plant is an integrated whole. Incidentally, if one can find a way to remove roots, such as by slicing through them near the tree trunk, a parallel set of underground experiments becomes available.

7.4 Successional progression

In species-rich tropical habitats, much of the fate of a plant is dependent on biotic interactions. The direction, path and speed of succession is highly variable and depends on the initial kind of disturbance, its intensity, proximity of other vegetation types, kind of vegetation removed, soil type, amount of seed in the soil, etc. Carefully replicated long-term experimental plots, whose design is such that their progress will indicate the relative importance of these variables, are needed. Such plots in the tropics must always be designed bearing in mind that the more species- and life-form-rich the vegetation, the more difficult it will be to identify any particularly small piece as 'climax vegetation'.

There is a large problem in deciding which of the multitude of characteristics of a successional sere to record. If there is to be replication of treatment, and more than 1 or 2 experimental variables, the number of traits recorded for each plot will have to be quite small. It is imperative that they be chosen so as to simultaneously test specific hypotheses about tropical succession such as:

(a) the speed at which the vegetation returns to something resembling the parental vegetation physiognomy is highly dependent on the life forms of the initial invading species,

(b) the number of species of reproducing plants in a successional sere is generally much less than the number of species of seeds that have arrived at the site,

(c) the poorer the soil, the less influence there will be on successional pattern if the herbivores are removed,

(d) the more species of plants in the region, the wider the array of possible successional progressions leading from a single major disturbance back to the original vegetation.

7.5 Post-dispersal fate of juveniles

It has long been a tradition in temperate zone plant ecology to determine why plants are where they are by correlating the presence of adults with various physical factors and then assuming that the causal processes have been identified. In the more species-rich parts of the tropics, this method (which is questionable in the best of circumstances) is next to worthless. Far more valuable is the direct observation of what happens to juvenile plants after they arrive in this or that habitat, and eventually relate this survival data to where the adults are found. Seeds and seedlings are easily moved about, and their competitors and herbivores can be manipulated relatively easily in many tropical habitats. The prime resource is simply the time needed to see what happens, for example, when the seeds of Costa Rican *Hymenaea courbaril* are dispersed onto limestone hills (the adults are found only on volcanic soils a few hundred metres away). There is no single reasonably complete published life table (a table showing age-specific fecundity and survival rates for a local population) for any tropical wild plant! While a theory of the impact of seed- and seedling-eating animals on a tropical forest is developing, there is almost no published data on exactly what is the fate of a seed as a function of its position in the seed shadow, proximity of other seed crops in time and space, activity of dispersal agents, etc. The entire area of the adaptive significance of seed germination time within and between seasons is a blank book for the tropics and yet incredibly easy to manipulate in the field.

7.6   Defences against vines

In view of the strongly debilitating effect of vines on self-supporting plants, many plants may be expected to have morphological and perhaps other defences against vines. This can be examined experimentally by construction of plant mimics with a variety of forms and placing them among stands of vines. Conversely, from the same experiments, it should be possible to discover the relative value of various climbing methods. Once the basic parameters seem to be identified, it should be possible to predict which self-supporting plants will have severe vine problems, of which types and in which habitats. Furthermore, by slight alterations of living plants, for example by tying artificial horizontal branches into them, it should be possible to discover other details of the interaction of vines with their substrate.

Of a closely parallel nature, but probably requiring much more time, should be the experimental modification of tree bark with respect to epiphyte establishment. This experimental work should go hand in hand with descriptive studies to determine why it is that trees of tropical deciduous forest, when transplanted to tropical rainforest, accumulate much larger loads of epiphytes than do rainforest trees. Simultaneously, an examination is needed of the possibility that tannins and other secondary compounds in tree bark interfere with epiphyte or parasite establishment.

7.7   Plant crown competition

Plant crowns clearly compete with each other for the area occupied by the crown. This is most conspicuous when two conspecific equal-sized crowns are adjacent and their crowns closely inter-digitate but do not overlap. Such competitive systems can be altered and initiated by pruning branches from carefully chosen portions of the crowns and then recording the pattern of re-colonization of the free space. There are some obvious variables that will enter into such a competition, such as the reproductive state of the two competitors, which tree the branch is cut from, how severe is the competition from other trees, etc. Badly needed is the converse experiment, done with the root 'crown'. While perhaps very difficult in the soil, it may well be that it could be done with ease with those species of epiphytes whose roots are spread over the surface of the tree branch. Here, not only removal, but mapping of the re-growth should be less destructive than underground. A note of caution is in order here. The value of a branch or root system is not necessarily linearly proportional to the area it covers, its biomass, its number of leaves, etc. Care will have to be exercised in choosing the appropriate parameters for measuring the outcome of a competitive event. Bear in mind that many parts of a plant are highly independent. Often, a shaded branch does not bear fruit even if its immediate insolated neighbours have a very heavy fruit load. The immediate cause of sterility may be hormone imbalance, but we are concerned here with why a physiology evolved that generates a hormone imbalance when a branch is shaded.

7.8   Rates of decomposition

It is apparent that decomposition rates of leaves, stems, and other debris are very habitat-specific. However, the inter-habitat variation in the tropics is almost totally undocumented. Further, species-specific decomposition rates within and between habitats are uncharted water in the tropics. Even the large amount of literature on timber decomposition trials (with respect to termites, fungi, beetles, etc.) is generally associated with undescribed habitats, and processed or seasoned wood. The technology of understanding litter decomposition can, in the first stages, require little more than nylon mesh bags to hold leaves of various sorts, and careful records of where various kinds of litter have been placed. The description of the various stages of decomposition needs careful thought and it is imperative that the origin and condition of the litter at the beginning of an observation period be carefully documented.

If chemical analysis methods are available, then changes in elements, energy, and secondary compounds are even more valuable. But simple questions, such as 'do the leaves from evergreen trees last longer than those from deciduous trees' are unanswered for the tropics. Of great interest would be simple tests of the effect of leachate from living foliage and litter on living plant roots and on animals. As with the previous studies, litter decomposition trials should be set so as to elucidate general hypotheses of ecology and tests of specific interactions. A simple experiment such as adding a potent fungicide to a litter decomposition trial is badly needed. If the habitats are chosen carefully with respect to such things as soil type, exposure to sun and rain, grazing mammals, etc., they can tell us much of the overall processes of the habitat.

7.9 Pollination

Lists of which animals visit which flowers are very low on the priorities of requirements in tropical pollination biology. On the other hand, it is still necessary to know which animals are actually carrying off pollen and, second, how far what portion of this pollen is carried. Direct observation of animals can be made, but pollen marked with powdered dye gives more conclusive results. By dyeing pollen on one plant, and then carefully examining the stigmas of neighbouring plants after the pollinators have been active, the most positive results are obtained. Information on pollen flow is the critical measure of pollinator efficiency here, rather than the number of fruit set.

Third, it must be known to what degree seed set is pollinator-limited, and in what habitats and circumstances. Especially important is knowing this for habitats where pollinator communities and the proportions of the plants they visit are still relatively intact, as compared with disturbed habitats (the usual site of contemporary pollination studies in the tropics). By hand pollinating, it is possible to determine exactly how many fruits the plant has the resources to produce. In undisturbed habitats it is likely that seed set is not pollinator-limited. The difficult problem then arises of analysing how selection has resulted in that size of flower crop which will lead to an optimum amount of pollen arriving from, and being donated to, other plants. Above all, these studies should abolish the notion that the size of the seed crop is a direct measure of pollinator 'efficiency'. As many tropical trees are dioecious, and even more appear to be obligate out-crossers, the documentation of the circumstances and constancy of these two traits is basic to tropical population biology. Data are needed on pollination within and between individuals, populations, and habitats.

7.10   Herbivore specificity

For the more zoologically oriented plant biologist, there is an immense uncharted sea in the tropics in the area of what animals eat what plant parts and plants, and when and where. For insects, this requires: (1) a sympathetic museum that will both agree to help identify *and* store the voucher specimens that are a *must*. However, most taxonomists are quite happy to identify specific insects known to feed on specific plants. (2) It requires two kinds of feeding information. It is necessary to known *where* species x is found feeding in the field and *in what frequency*. Furthermore, it must be known with what *sample technique* the data was collected. It is essential then to know on what plants the herbivore will grow to maturity in the lab; the plants tested should be those which are found in the insect's habitat, but do not appear to be normally eaten. In the laboratory studies, great care must be taken to describe not only the kinds of food offered and eaten (old leaves, new leaves, sun leaves, leaves from a sick tree, etc.) but the physical conditions of the feeding arenas. (3) This type of information should be available for a few herbivore species across many habitats. (4) The same facts should be known for the total array of herbivores in one carefully chosen habitat. (5) The information should also be obtained for a few carefully chosen plant species within one habitat (and eventually across many habitats for these species). At present, not even a reasonably accurate list can be produced of the insects that feed on a single species of wild tropical plant, to say nothing of how much damage each does. With the exception of a few commercially important insects in highly disturbed habitats, not one thorough study has been carried out of the foods of a widely distributed wild tropical herbivore over its entire range.

Suggested Reading

ASHTON, P. S. (1969). Speciation among tropical forest trees: some deductions in the light of recent evidence. *Biol. J. Linn. Soc.*, **1**, 155–196.

BAKER, H. G. (1970). Evolution in the tropics. *Biotropica*, **2**, 101–111.

BAWA, K. S. (1974). Breeding systems of tree species of a lowland tropical community and their evolutionary significance. *Evolution, N.Y.*. **28**. 85–92.

BROWER, L. P. and BROWER, J. V. Z. (1964). Birds, butterflies, and plant poisons: a study in ecological chemistry. *Zoologica, N.Y.*, **49**, 137–159.

BUDOWSKI, G. (1970). The distinction between old secondary and climax species in tropical Central American lowland forest. *Bull. int. Soc. trop. Ecol.*, **11**, 44–48.

CASWELL, H., REED, F., STEPHENSON, S. N. and WERNER, P. A. (1973). Photosynthetic pathways and selective herbivory: a hypothesis. *Am. Nat.*, **107**, 465–501.

CHERRETT, J. M. (1972). Chemical aspects of plant attack by leaf-cutting ants. In *Phytochemical ecology*, HARBORNE, J. B., ed. Academic Press, London, p. 13–24.

CONNELL, J. H. (1971). On the role of natural enemies in preventing competitive exclusion in some marine animals and in rain forest trees. *In* The dynamics of populations, DEN BOER, P. J. and GRADWELL, G. R., eds., *Proc. Adv. Study Inst.* on 'Dynamics of numbers in populations', Oosterbeek, Netherlands, p. 298–312.

DOCTERS VAN LEEUWEN, W. M. (1954). On the biology of some Loranthaceae and the role birds play in their life-history. *Beaufortia*, **4**, 105–208.

DODSON, C. H., DRESSLER, R. L., HILLS, H. G., ADAMS, R. M. and WILLIAMS, N. H. (1969). Biologically active compounds in orchid fragrances. *Science, N.Y.*, **164**, 1243–1249.

FAEGRI, K. and VAN DER PIJL, L. (1966). *The principles of pollination biology.* Pergamon Press, Oxford, 248 pp.

FRANKIE, G. W., BAKER, H. G. and OPLER, P. A. (1974). Comparative phenological studies of trees in tropical Wet and Dry forests in the lowlands of Costa Rica. *J. Ecol.*, **62**, 881–919.

GILBERT, L. E. and RAVEN, P. H., eds. (1975). *Coevolution of animals and plants.* University of Texas Press, Austin, 246 pp

HAFFER, J. (1969). Speciation in Amazonian forest birds. *Science, N.Y.*, **165**, 131–137.

HARPER, J. C., LOVELL, P. H. and MOORE, K. G. (1970). The shapes and sizes of seeds. *A. Rev. Ecol. Syst.*, **1**, 327–356.

HARPER, J. L. (1967). A Darwinian approach to plant ecology. *J. Ecol.*, **55**, 247–270.

HEINRICH, B. and RAVEN, P. H. (1972). Energetics and pollination ecology. *Science, N.Y.*, **176**, 597–602.

HOLTTUM, R. E. (1961). *Plant life in Malaya.* Longmans, Green and Co., London, 254 pp.

JAMIESON, B. G. M. and REYNOLDS, J. F. (1967). *Tropical plant types.* Pergamon, Oxford, 347 pp.

JANZEN, D. H. (1970). Herbivores and the number of tree species in tropical forests. *Am. Nat.*, **104**, 501–528.

JANZEN, D. H. (1971). Escape of juvenile *Dioclea megacarpa* (Leguminosae) vines from predators in a deciduous tropical forest. *Am. Nat.*, **105**, 97–112.

JANZEN, D. H. (1971). Euglossine bees as long-distance pollinators of tropical plants. *Science, N.Y.*, **171**, 203–205.

JANZEN, D. H. (1972). Escape in space by *Sterculia apetala* seeds from the bug *Dysdercus fasciatus* in a Costa Rican deciduous forest. *Ecology*, **53**, 350–361.

JANZEN, D. H. (1973). Dissolution of mutualism between *Cecropia* and its *Azteca* ants. *Biotropica*, **5**, 15–28.

JANZEN, D. H. (1973). Sweep samples of tropical foliage insects: effects of seasons, vegetation types, elevation, time of day, and insularity. *Ecology*, **54**, 687–708.

JANZEN, D. H. (1974). Tropical blackwater rivers, animals and mast fruiting by the Dipterocarpaceae. *Biotropica* **6**, 69–103.

KEAY, R. W. J. (1957). Wind dispersal of some species in a Nigerian rainforest. *J. Ecol.*, **45**, 471–478.

KERFOOT, O. (1963). The root systems of tropical forest trees. *Commonw. For. Rev.*, **42**, 19–26.

MORTON, E. S. (1973). On the evolutionary advantages and disadvantages of fruit eating in tropical birds. *Am. Nat.*, **107**, 8–22.

OPPENHEIMER, J. R. and LANG, G. E. (1969). Cebus monkeys: effect on branching of *Gustavia* trees. *Science, N.Y.*, **165**, 187–188.

RAMIREZ, W. (1970). Host specificity of fig wasps (Agaonidae). *Evolution, N.Y.*, **24**, 680–691.

REHR, S. S., BELL, E.A., JANZEN, D. H. and FEENY, P. P. (1973). Insecticidal amino acids in legume seeds. *Biochem. Syst.*, **1**, 63–67.

REHR, S. S., FEENY, P. P. and JANZEN, D. H. (1973). Chemical defense in Central American non-ant-acacias. *J. Anim. Ecol.*, **42**, 405–416.

RICHARDS, P. W. (1952). *The tropical rainforest.* Cambridge University Press, Cambridge, 450 pp.

RICHARDS, P. W. (1970). *The life of the jungle.* McGraw-Hill, New York, 232 pp.

ROCKWOOD, L. L. (1973). Distribution, density, and dispersion of two species of *Atta* in Guanacaste Province, Costa Rica. *J. Anim. Ecol.*, **42**, 803–817.

ROCKWOOD, L. L. (1973). The effect of defoliation on seed production of six Costa Rican tree species. *Ecology*, **54**, 1363–1369.

SARMIENTO, G. (1972). Ecological and floristic convergences between seasonal plant formations of tropical and subtropical South America. *J. Ecol.*, **60**, 367–410.

SCHLISING, R. A. (1970). Sequence and timing of bee foraging in flowers of *Ipomoea* and *Aniseai* (Convolvulaceae). *Ecology*, **51**, 1061–1067.

SMYTHE, N. (1970). Relationship between fruiting seasons and seed dispersal methods in a neotropical forest. *Am. Nat.*, **104**, 25–35.

SNOW, D. W. (1966). A possible selective factor in the evolution of fruiting seasons in a tropical forest. *Oikos*, **15**, 274–281.

SPATZ, G. and MUELLER-DOMBOIS, D. (1973). The influence of feral goats on koa tree reproduction in Hawaii Volcanoes National Park. *Ecology*, **54**, 870–876.

STILES, F. C. (1925). Ecology, flowering phenology, and hummingbird pollination of some Costa Rican *Heliconia* species. *Ecology*, **56**, 285–301.

TERBOUGH, J. (1973). On the notion of favorableness in plant ecology. *Am. Nat.*, **107**, 481–501.

TOMLINSON, P. B. and GILL, A. M. (1973). Growth habits of tropical trees: some guiding principles. In *Tropical forest ecosystems in Africa and South America: a comparative review*, MEGGERS, B. J., AYENSU, E. S. and DUCKWORTH, W. D., eds., pp. 129–143.

VAN DER PIJL, L. (1953). The shedding of leaves and branches of some tropical trees. *Idon. J. for Nat. Sci.*, **109**, 11–25.

VAN DER PIJL, L. (1972). *Principles of dispersal in higher plants.* Springer-Verlag, Berlin, 161 pp.

VUILLEUMIER, B. S. (1971). Pleistocene changes in the fauna and flora of South America. *Science*, **173**, 771–780.

WALTER, H. (1971). *Ecology of tropical and subtropical vegetation.* Oliver & Boyd, Edinburgh. 539 pp.

WHITTAKER, R. H. and FEENY, P. P. (1971). Allelochemics: chemical interactions between species. *Science*, **171**, 757–770.

WILSON, D. E. and JANZEN, D. H. (1972). Predation on *Scheelea* palm seeds by bruchids: seed density and distance from the parent. *Ecology*, **53**, 954–959.

WOLCOTT, G. N. (1946). Factors in the natural resistance of woods to termite attack. *Carrib. Forester*, **7**, 121–134.